LISTEN TO A TALE

**Illustrated by Eric Kincaid
Eric Rowe and Gill Embleton**

BRIMAX BOOKS · NEWMARKET · ENGLAND

ISBN 0 86112 290 9
© Brimax Books Ltd 1986. All rights reserved.
Published by Brimax Books, Newmarket, England 1986
The stories and illustrations in this collection
have also appeared in the 'Tell a Tale' series,
the 'Read Once Again' series and in 'Tales of
Magic and Make-Believe'.
Printed in Hong Kong.

Contents

Rumpelstiltskin

Once there was a miller who had a beautiful daughter. He was always talking about her and saying how clever she was.

One day, the miller had to take some flour to the palace. He told the king about his daughter.

"Her hair is like spun gold, Your Majesty, and what is more, she is so clever she can spin straw into gold."

This was not true. The miller's daughter had never even spun cloth but the king did not know this.

"Bring your daughter to me!" said the king.

The miller almost danced down the steps of the palace. He took his daughter to see the king the very next day.

The king led her into a room where there was a pile of straw, a stool and a spinning wheel.

"Now," said the king. "You must spin this straw into gold by dawn tomorrow or you shall die."

He left the room and locked the door.

The miller's daughter could not understand. How could she spin straw into gold? How could she spin anything? She did not even know how to begin. She crept into a corner of the room and burst into tears.

Suddenly, there was a puff of smoke and a strange little man stood beside her. His face was brown and wrinkled, his nose was long and his white beard almost reached his knobbly knees.

"What's the matter?" he said. "Why are you crying?"

"Whatever shall I do?" the girl said tearfully. "Look at all this straw! The king has said I must spin it into gold by early morning or I shall die! I cannot even spin!"

"Dry your tears," said the little man. "What will you give me if I spin it for you?"

The girl's fingers touched the necklace she was wearing.

"I will give you my necklace," she said.

The strange little man clapped his hands with delight. He sat down to spin. The spinning wheel whirled round. It made a gentle humming sound. The girl's eyes closed and she fell asleep.

While she slept, the straw became a pile of gold. She awoke; the strange little man had vanished.

In the morning, the king could not believe his eyes. A heap of shining gold! "Come with me," he said at once. The king led the girl into a much larger room, which was filled with even more straw. He told her she must spin it into gold by the next day.

Once again the door was locked and the poor girl began to cry. Once more there was a puff of smoke and there stood the strange little man.

"What will you give me this time if I spin the straw?" he asked.

"Oh, thank you, thank you," she said. "I will give you the ring my mother gave me." She slipped the ring off her finger and held it out to him. Without another word, he took it and started to spin.

The next day, although the king was delighted with the gold, he was not satisfied. He took the miller's daughter into a larger room with heaps of straw which nearly reached the ceiling.

"Now, my dear," he said. "Spin all this straw into gold tonight and I will make you my queen."

This time, the girl was very frightened. She knew that if the little man appeared, she had nothing left to give him.

Once again there was a puff of smoke and there he stood. As if he knew already, the strange little man said, "Promise me that when you are queen, you will give me your first baby. If you promise, I will spin the straw for you."

'How can I promise?' she thought. 'I may never be queen . . . or have a child . . . but it's the only way to get the spinning done.'

"I promise," she whispered.

The strange little man spun the straw into gold and vanished as before.

Next day, the king kept his word. He married the miller's daughter and she became queen.

Some years later, the queen sat smiling at her first baby. A voice behind her said, "Remember your promise? I have come for the child." It was the strange little man.

"Oh, no! Do not make me give you my baby!" she begged. "Take all my other treasure, but let me keep him! Please, please!"

"I will give you one chance," he said. "You have three days in which to tell me my name. If you find my right name, you may keep the child."

The queen wrote down every name she could think of and sent her servants out to find new names.

"Is it William? . . . David? . . . Rupert?" she asked, when the little man came the next day. To each one he replied, "That is not my name."

On the second day, she tried funny names like Cross-Patch, Double-Dutch and Hanky-Panky, but still he replied, "That is not my name."

On the third morning, a servant rushed in to see the queen.

"Your Majesty!" he said. "I was in the forest . . . there was a little hut with a fire outside. A strange little man was hopping round it and singing!"

"What was he singing?" asked the queen.

"He sang something like this, Your Majesty . . .

'I will dance and I will sing
Tomorrow will the baby bring
The queen she cannot spoil my game
For Rumpelstiltskin is my name!'"

The queen was so happy when she heard this. She gave the servant a bag of gold.

When the strange little man came, he asked, "Well, my lady, what is my name?"

"James, perhaps?" said the queen. "Richard?"

"No, no," replied the strange little man.

"Rumpelstiltskin then?" said the queen slowly.

The strange little man howled with rage and stamped so hard that his foot sank right through the floor.

"Who told you my name? A witch? Yes, a witch!" he shouted. With a great puff of smoke and in a flash the strange little man was gone. No one ever saw him again.

Jodi's Giant Egg

When Jodi was nine years old, he went to live with his aunt in a little village called Fenelon. Aunt Martha was a widow, who made a living by selling her fruit, vegetables and eggs. She gave Jodi the job of feeding the hens.

Jodi soon made friends with Max, the farmer's son. One day, when the two boys went for a walk outside the village, Jodi found a large egg beside the road.

"It's enormous!" said Max. "I wonder what kind of bird laid that?"

Jodi grinned. "An albatross?" He picked the egg up carefully. It was very heavy.

"You're not going to take it home!" said Max in surprise.

"Yes I am. My pet hen will hatch it. She is sitting on six eggs already," said Jodi.

Aunt Martha was busy when the boys returned, so she did not see Jodi creep into the henhouse and slip the egg under the speckled hen.

For a week, nothing happened. Then one morning, as Jodi opened the henhouse door, he heard a loud squawking. The hen was hiding in a corner clucking. All six chicks had hatched, but in the middle of them stood a funny-looking bird, with a long neck, flat head and awkward spindly legs.

Jodi ran to fetch Max. "Whatever could it be?" he whispered. "An eagle?"

"We'll ask Captain Gringe," said Max. "He has been right round the world."

Jodi picked up the bird and they went round to the old sea
captain's house, which had portholes for windows and a fixed telescope
on the roof.

"Why, it's an ostrich," said the Captain. "I saw lots of them in
Africa. Where did you find this one?" Jodi told him about the egg.

"I wonder how it got there?" The Captain rubbed his chin
thoughtfully.

"Will it grow very big?" asked Jodi, stroking the bird. There
was a twinkle in the old sailor's blue eyes as he said, "Eight feet
high, at least!"

The boys stared at one another in dismay. They were thinking
of Aunt Martha. Jodi had to plead with her to let him keep the
ostrich.

"He is not to go near the chickens, mind," she warned. "And you are responsible for him."

Jodi called his pet Oz. The strange bird grew very quickly. In less than a month, he was taller than Jodi and his body was covered with lovely black feathers. His wings were white.

Poor Jodi found it hard to keep him out of trouble, for his pet had an enormous appetite and Oz would eat anything. He ran about the village, helping himself from market stalls or reaching into store windows. Jodi, panting after him, could not catch up in time to stop him. When he did, Oz had swallowed everything, including wrappings. Often his neck looked a very odd shape indeed.

The store-keepers were always shaking their fists at Oz and warning him off. He was noisy, a nuisance and always in someone's way, but the people in the village were secretly proud of him – theirs was the only village with an ostrich.

Oz went everywhere with Jodi, even to school. The schoolmaster found him a tall stool and he sat at the back of the class. At night, he slept on the floor of Jodi's room, his head on a cushion, his body covered with an old patchwork bedspread.

In a grand house near the village lived the Duchess of Fenelon.

One day Oz disappeared. When Jodi found him, he had eaten every flower in her garden.

"This bird must go!" she shouted at Jodi. "I will give you one week to get rid of him or I shall have him for dinner!"

The villagers were upset but they knew that the Duchess meant what she said. Jodi could not bear to part with Oz. Besides, where could he go?

Next morning, Oz was pecking at the moss which covered an old ruin near the village, when a stone stuck in his throat. He ran home to Jodi, squawking in fright.

"Take him to Doctor Finkle," said Max. But the doctor had nothing long enough to reach the stone.

"I know," cried Jodi, "we will borrow Professor Crank's violin bow!"

They went off to find the old music teacher who said, "Lend my bow to pull a stone out of an ostrich's throat? Certainly not!"

"But Oz will choke!" cried Jodi, nearly in tears.

The Professor was a kindly man, so he handed the bow to Jodi and the boys raced back to the doctor's house. Poor Oz had turned purple.

"Lie down, Oz, and open your beak wide," said the doctor.

The stone was out in no time and Oz returned to his normal colour.

The doctor looked at the stone and said, "Where did you say it came from?"

"I don't know," said Jodi. "Oz was by himself."

"Come and show us, Oz," said the doctor.

Oz led the way to the crumbling wall of the ruin and stretched up to a high ledge. "It's all very well for birds with long necks," said the doctor, "but we cannot see up there."

Jodi was already climbing the moss-covered wall. He swung his leg over the top and scraped off some of the moss with his fingers.

"It is all like that stone," he called. "White with swirly patterns."

The doctor's eyes were shining. "It is a marble wall," he said. "We must tell the Duchess."

"The moss must be cleaned off at once," she ordered.

Soon everyone in the village was busy with ladders, rakes and brooms, removing the ivy, moss and other creepers which had covered the wall for hundreds of years. Oz was a great help reaching the high corners.

Four days later, they all stood round admiring a beautiful castle made of marble. The Duchess who never smiled, was beaming with delight. "People will come from far and wide to see this," she said and she was right. Soon visitors were pouring into the little village to be shown the marble castle. The Duchess had not forgotten about Oz.

"I am going to have a statue made of that bird," she said. "We would never have discovered the marble castle if it had not been for him."

Jodi was delighted and so was Oz.

So now, when visitors come to the village, the first things they see are two ostriches eight feet high in the middle of the square. One has a stone at its feet on which is written, HERE STANDS OZ, DISCOVERER OF THE MARBLE CASTLE OF FENELON. The other ostrich, who looks just like him, is Oz himself.

Seeing is Believing

Once there was a wizard who sometimes left his secret room and went into the market place. He liked entertaining people with his tricks. They enjoyed it, and so did he.

"Roll up! Roll up!" he cried one day. "Come and see my magic bird!" It wasn't long before a crowd had collected.

"Come on then, show us what it can do!" shouted a boy who was carrying a plank of wood on his shoulder.

"Lend me your plank for a minute or two," said the wizard.

"It won't come to any harm, will it?" asked the boy.

"Of course not. Put it on the ground," said the wizard. He took a cockerel from a sack and put it on the ground beside the plank.

"Watch carefully," he said. He fluttered his fingers over the cockerel and chanted some strange words. To the astonishment of the crowd the cockerel lifted the plank with its beak and began to strut up and down with it.

"How can it do that?" cried the boy whose plank it was. "That's heavy. . .I know. . .I've been carrying it."

Oohs and aahs of astonishment swept through the crowd like a gust of wind.

A girl at the edge of the crowd stood on her tiptoes so that she could see better.

"What's clever about that?" she said. "Any cockerel is strong enough to pick up a straw!" The girl had a four-leaf clover in her hand and could see things exactly as they were. The wizard's magic had fooled everyone else, but it didn't fool her.

Her words were enough to break the spell, and then everyone saw that the cockerel was carrying a straw.

"Cheat! Cheat!" they shouted. The poor wizard, who had only been trying to entertain them, was pelted with cabbages and rotten tomatoes and chased out of town. How everyone laughed at his discomfort. The girl with the four-leaf clover laughed loudest of all.

The months passed, and then one day, there was a village wedding. The villagers were walking in procession across the fields, to the church where the wedding was to be held, when those behind tripped over the heels of those in front. The procession had stopped.

"What is it? What is happening?" asked the people at the back as they jostled to the front to see what was wrong.

They had come to a stream which was far too wide to jump across. There was no bridge over it, and no plank with which to make a bridge.

"We'll have to go back the way we have come, and take the long way round to the church," they cried.

"No! No, we can't do that. I'll be late for my wedding," cried the bride, who was the girl who had found the four-leaf clover.

"Then what shall we do!" they asked her.

In answer the bride kicked off her shoes. She bundled her skirt round her knees and stepped into the stream.

"Brrr . . . it's very cold," she shivered. "Ouch! It's very stony," she winced as she carefully stepped her way across.

"Do not get your wedding dress wet," called the onlookers, those that is, who were not running as fast as their legs would take them the long way round to the church. They began taking off their own shoes, and tucking up their own skirts. The men rolled up their trouser legs. Soon, everyone was wincing and shivering as they followed the bride.

"Where are your eyes that you think that is water?" asked a mocking voice.

All eyes turned towards the bank. They saw the familiar face of the wizard. All eyes looked downwards. Instead of water they were wading through grass and blue flax flowers. They were holding their shoes above their heads. They were all showing their knees. The wizard was having the last laugh, and now it was they who had the red faces. How foolish they looked and how foolish they felt.

Poet, Goblin and Donkey

Once there was a poet who could make up songs that would entice the fish from the sea, the birds from the sky, and the worms from the ground. The words he sang were as magical as any spell.

One day, the Queen's daughter fell into a sulk. The Queen sent for the poet.

"Your Majesty," he said, bowing very low. "Can I be of service?"

"The Princess woke this morning with a pimple on the end of her nose," said the Queen. "The only thing I know of that will cure it is the magic . . . "

"Oh, how kind," interrupted the poet. "How kind to say the magic of my songs will charm away a pimple and restore the Princess to her former beauty . . . "

"Don't interrupt . . . " said the Queen. "That wasn't what I was going to say at all. The only thing that will cure it in time for the ball tonight, is the magic ointment owned by the Goblin of the Rock. I command you to go and get it."

"But the goblin hasn't been seen for at least a hundred years," said the poet. "He NEVER leaves the rock."

"Then try your magic songs on him . . . " said the Queen.

It was a royal command, so the poet had to go.

The goblin was curled into a tight ball in the very heart of the rock. He was deaf to the world, or so everyone thought.

The poet knew it was going to be difficult. He knew he would have to sing as he had never sung before. He sang softly with strange mysterious words, and at last there was a faint stirring inside the rock. Presently the top of the goblin's bald little head began to show. The poet could see his forehead . . . then two slanting eyes . . . then a long pointed nose . . . then thin lips . . . and a round chin. Then two knobbly shoulders appeared.

The poet was drawing the goblin from the rock as gently and as surely as a maiden draws a fine thread from a bundle of flax. Now the tops of the goblin's spindly arms were showing . . . now his bony elbows . . . now the poet could see the hand holding the precious bowl of ointment . . .

At that precise moment a donkey brayed, right beside the poet's elbow. "EEE! AAWWW!" The poet's song had charmed HIM out of his stable, across a field, over a stream, through a wood, over a hill . . .

"EEE! AWW!" he brayed again, as though to say, "I've come!"

The poet was startled out of his wits and fell over backwards. The goblin was so frightened he shot high into the air in a tangle of arms and legs and rock dust.

Before the poet could recover his senses enough to catch him the goblin had disappeared into a new hiding place carrying the precious ointment with him.

And that's how it was that a proud princess went to a ball hiding the pimple on the end of her nose behind a fan.

It all goes to show that a poet's spell can be broken as easily as any other spell and that sometimes a poet can be too clever by half.

Mr Boffin's Bubble

"Just look at that," said Mr Boffin happily. On the table in front of him was a shiny bubble about as big as a golf ball. It was Mr Boffin's bubble and it had taken him over a week to make it. Using his special copper saucepan, he had mixed together Bubbly Goo made with soap, thistle-down, early morning dew, a tablespoonful of moonlight, a bit of 'this and that' out of his surprise box and finally, a good pinch of Inventors' Dust. After much boiling and bubbling, there was only a sticky drop left. Mr Boffin turned the saucepan upside down, the drop slid out and grew into this splendid bubble, all shiny and glistening.

Suddenly, as he bent over it, his nose tickled. ATISHOO! he sneezed and away flew the bubble. Out through the open window it went and disappeared from sight.

"Oh no!" cried Mr Boffin, leaping to his feet. "Whatever will happen now?"

He knew he had made a special bubble. Anything and everything it touched within the next hour would change in some way. After that the bubble would burst and vanish – or so it should.

Mr Boffin leaned out of the open window and saw his cat asleep in the flowerbed. Instead of being covered in fur, the poor cat was now covered in feathers!

A bird in a nearby tree was almost falling off the branch – imagine seeing a cat with feathers! He couldn't wait for the cat to wake up.

The bubble bounced along enjoying itself. It had only about one hour of freedom and it meant to have as much fun as it could.

In a terrible state, Mr Boffin rushed out into the street to see if he could catch it. Wiping his face with his handkerchief, he began to feel worried. What had he done? Where had it gone?

Mrs Gossip and Mrs Chatter were busy talking as usual about everyone in the village. The bubble floated between their nodding heads, gently brushing past them. The sound of their voices stopped at once. They went on talking, of course, but no sound came from their mouths at all. 'Do them good,' thought the bubble – 'give everyone a rest for a bit.'

The breeze bounced the bubble up to an open window and it heard a boy say crossly, "I can't play it. I won't play it. I hate it." Passing into the room, the bubble saw a woman and a little boy sitting at a piano. There was a crash of chords as the boy angrily banged his hands down on the keys.

The bubble passed across the boy's hands before drifting back to the open window. "How funny," said the boy. "I thought I saw a soapy bubble come through the window and across my hands. Did you see it, Miss Archer?"

"Yes John, I did, but it's gone now," replied his music teacher. "Come, please try again. Play once more."

"I will. My hands don't feel hot and sticky any more," said John and he played the piece correctly this time.

33

'Wheeeeeee' went the bubble as it rose up into the air and touched the clock face on the church tower. The clock stopped at once. 'Ha! Ha!' laughed the bubble. 'That will give everybody something to think about!'

It floated down and in through the dairy window, bouncing merrily along the milk bottles that were in the crates. At once the milk inside them became solid.

'I shouldn't have done that,' thought the bubble when it saw the customers waiting to buy milk. It heard their cries of dismay when they found the bottles almost too heavy to lift. Quickly moving sideways, then backwards, the bubble drifted outside again.

Time was running out. The bubble's hour was nearly over. It saw Mr Boffin standing outside the school gates. He looked hot and upset. Gliding behind Mr Boffin, the bubble sailed in through an open ground-floor window.

It was a hot day and both the children and their teacher would be glad when it was time to go home. In front of the teacher's desk was a pile of exercise books. The children had done their homework very badly. The teacher was not pleased with them.

The bubble bounced on the books and up into the air. It liked children and this was a chance to make them happy – anyway until tomorrow! The teacher tried to pick up the top exercise book but found they were all stuck together. He could not separate them. Suddenly he felt tired. Sitting at their desks, the class watched him carefully. They noticed the bouncy bubble as it went past the teacher's open mouth.

"Pay attention," he said, but the children heard nothing, for the poor man could not make a sound. His voice had gone. The children stared at him. The teacher picked up a piece of chalk and wrote on the blackboard CLASS DISMISS.

The boys and girls could not believe their luck. He had forgotten all about their homework. He had lost his voice and they could go home now. Gratefully, chattering and clattering, they rose to their feet and left the classroom.

Standing outside the school, Mr Boffin suddenly saw the bubble come through the window. Rushing forward, he tried to catch it but the bubble slipped through his fingers.

'Aha,' thought the bubble as it saw Mr Boffin. 'This is my last chance and it's too good to miss.'

In a moment its fun time would end and it couldn't resist bobbing up right into Mr Boffin's face which was bending over the bubble. Oh, it really was going to enjoy doing this! Quick, it was going to pop, and it did, on the end of Mr Boffin's nose.

'PLOP . . . SPLOOF' went the bubble and burst right in Mr Boffin's face.

"My goodness, whatever is happening?" cried Mr Boffin, as suddenly whiskers sprouted on his chin. He found he was growing a big, bushy beard and moustache. It looked very funny and the children running out of the school laughed at him.

Whatever changes the bubble might have made on its travels, Mr Boffin hoped that everything would soon return to what it was before – including his whiskery face. What was the end of the recipe for making his bubble? That would help, but oh dear, he had forgotten to write it down and now he couldn't remember!

Big and Little

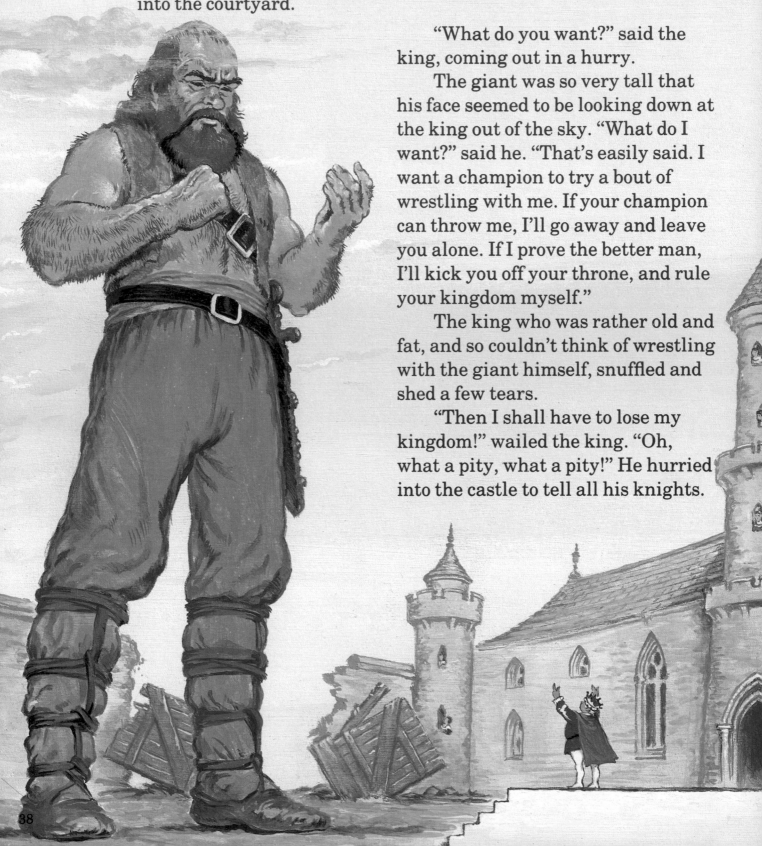

Once upon a time Big the giant came to the king's palace, and banged on the gates. The gates fell down with a crash, and he strode into the courtyard.

"What do you want?" said the king, coming out in a hurry.

The giant was so very tall that his face seemed to be looking down at the king out of the sky. "What do I want?" said he. "That's easily said. I want a champion to try a bout of wrestling with me. If your champion can throw me, I'll go away and leave you alone. If I prove the better man, I'll kick you off your throne, and rule your kingdom myself."

The king who was rather old and fat, and so couldn't think of wrestling with the giant himself, snuffled and shed a few tears.

"Then I shall have to lose my kingdom!" wailed the king. "Oh, what a pity, what a pity!" He hurried into the castle to tell all his knights.

Sitting on a little velvet stool was Little the dwarf whom the king kept near him to make him laugh when he was sad. When he saw the king in tears, he puffed out his little chest and said, "Leave the giant to me. I'll deal with him!"

"You!" said the king, and he and his knights laughed and laughed. "Why, he could crush you with his little finger!"

"Not so," said Little. "It is I who can twist him round my little finger." He took a sponge full of water and a bag of flour, and out he strutted into the courtyard.

The giant was getting impatient. "I can't wait here all day," said he. "Has the king chosen his champion?"

"I am his champion," said Little, sticking out his chest.

The giant doubled up with laughter. He laughed so loud that all the windows in the palace rattled and a lot of glass fell out.

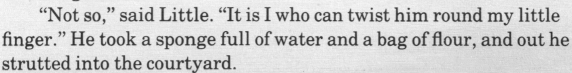

39

"Fight first, and laugh last," said Little, "if there's anything left of you to laugh with. But, before we fight, we'll have a trial of strength. You show me what you can do and I'll show you what I can do. Can you squeeze water out of a stone?"

The giant picked up a stone and squeezed it so hard between his hands that a few drops of water oozed out of it. "See that?" said he. "Is your head harder than that stone, dwarf?"

"Pooh!" said Little. He, too, picked up a stone. He squeezed the stone between his palms, and a whole stream of water ran over his hands and down onto the ground. "Is your head harder than this stone, giant?" said he.

Big the giant stared. The dwarf had the sponge in his hands as well as the stone and the water was running out of the sponge, but the giant didn't know that.

He picked up another stone and flung it onto the ground with such a crack that it crumbled to dust. "See that?" said he. "When we come to wrestle that is what your body will be like."

"Pooh!" said Little. He picked up a stone and flung it into the air, and such a cloud of white dust fell down all round him that he was completely hidden by it.

The giant stared harder than ever. He couldn't turn a stone to dust merely by flinging it into the air. Neither could the dwarf. He had thrown the bag of flour as well as the stone: but, of course, the giant didn't know that.

"You see?" said the dwarf. "So will your body be when we come to wrestle, giant, but I feel almost ashamed to wrestle with such a weakling as you!"

The giant began to think he had got the worst of the bargain. "You are the strongest little dwarf I have ever come across!" said he. "We won't wrestle after all. For then I should have to kill you and all your strength would be wasted. Tell you what – you come home and live with me."

"I don't mind if I do," said the dwarf. So Big the giant carried him all the way to his house.

In the giant's kitchen there was an oven as big as a barn and in the oven there were loaves of bread as big as tables. The giant put a loaf on the table, and they sat down to eat.

Now the giant was an untidy eater. He crammed his mouth so full of bread that some of it went down the wrong way.

He gave a cough and a sneeze and the sneeze made such a draught that the dwarf was blown up to the ceiling. He just managed to catch hold of a beam, and there he hung.

The giant looked up in surprise. "What are you doing up there?" he spluttered.

"Be quiet!" said the dwarf crossly. "You sneezed! If you do such a rude thing again, I shall pull out this beam and break it over your head."

"I'm very sorry," said Big the giant. "I didn't know it was rude. Come on down and – A-tish-ooo!!"

He sneezed again and this time Little was blown off the beam and whirled right through the open window. He fell on some long grass so he wasn't hurt. He picked himself up and walked back through the door.

"This is really too much!" he cried. "I can't stand such manners! I am going back to the king."

"Oh, don't do that," said the giant. "I've never met a little fellow I like as much as you and I don't want to live alone any longer."

"No, I've made up my mind," said the little dwarf. "If ever you come bothering the king again, you know what to expect. I shall throw you up in the air and bring you down turned to dust – just you see if I don't. Goodbye."

The giant stood at the door and stared after him. He felt so lonely that he wanted to cry but he went into the kitchen and drank all his wine and then he felt better.

It took the little dwarf a long time to get home but he reached the king's palace at long last.

The king was very pleased to see him and felt so grateful when he heard that the giant was never coming back. He decided that he would build the dwarf a little palace of his own with all the furniture just the right size for him. He gave him a suit of cloth of gold, and a suit of cloth of silver but the one he liked best of all was the one of green velvet trimmed with pearls. He had little page boys to wait on him, and a little carriage drawn by the smallest of small white ponies to ride out in. He had a little wife too, for the king would not rest until he found a little lady small enough to be his bride.

So Little and his wife lived together for the rest of their lives in their own little palace.

Little Red Riding Hood

Red Riding Hood lived with her mother in a little cottage on the edge of a wood. Her grandmother lived on the other side of the wood.

One day her mother gave Red Riding Hood a basket of nice things to eat: butter, honey and new-laid eggs.

"Take these to Grandma," said her mother. "She is not well. Keep to the path now. Give Grandma my love and then come home."

"I will," said Red Riding Hood. She waved goodbye.

It was a lovely sunny morning. Red Riding Hood was humming to herself as she came to the wood. She looked very pretty in her red hood and cloak. The birds peeped through the leaves to see her pass. The robin even sang a song for her. A squirrel at the top of a tree stopped nibbling a nut – just to watch her.

When Red Riding Hood came to the middle of the wood she stopped to pick some flowers. A wolf came along the path to meet her.

"Good morning, my dear," he said. "Where are you going?"

"I am going to see my Grandma," said Red Riding Hood. "She is not well."

"Oh dear," said the wolf kindly. "I am sorry. Have you far to go?"

"Just to the cottage at the end of this path," said Red Riding Hood.

"Well," said the wolf, "I'll say good-day; I am going down this way. I hope your Grandma feels better soon . . . Goodbye!"

Red Riding Hood went on her way, but the wolf did not keep to his path. He turned round and ran along another one to get to Grandma's cottage first.

Grandma saw him coming, and hid under her bed. Her nightcap fell on to the floor.

In came the wolf. He put the nightcap on and climbed into bed.

When Red Riding Hood came to the cottage door, she lifted the latch and walked in. She went over to her Grandma's bed and sat down.

"Look, Grandma, I've brought you lots of nice things to eat . . . Shall I put them in the cupboard?" There was no answer.

When Red Riding Hood turned towards Grandma again, two staring eyes, under a nightcap, watched her from the pillow. The frilly nightcap had slipped and she could see one large ear. 'How Grandma has changed,' thought Red Riding Hood.

"Oh, Grandma," she whispered, "what big ears you have!"

"All the better to hear you with, my dear," said the wolf.

How strange Grandma sounded.

"Oh, Grandma, what big eyes you have!"

"All the better to see you with, my dear," said the wolf with a smile.

"Oh, Grandma," said Red Riding Hood, "what big teeth you have!"

"All the better to EAT you with!" said the wolf. He leapt out of the bed, and tried to catch her.

Red Riding Hood screamed. She ran as fast as she could out of the house and down the path into the wood.

Two woodcutters were busy cutting down trees. They heard Red Riding Hood calling for help. At once, they left their work and chased the wolf.

How he ran when he saw the men coming after him! How funny he looked with Grandma's frilly nightcap flapping up and down on one ear! They all watched until the wolf had gone. He was never seen again.

Red Riding Hood was so glad.

"Will you help me to find my Grandma, please?" she asked her woodcutter friends.

"Of course we will," they said. Then hand in hand, they all went back to Grandma's cottage.

They looked everywhere for Grandma, but could not find her. They were not looking in the right place, were they?

"Grandma!" called Red Riding Hood. "Where are you . . . ?"

"I am here!" said a small voice, and then came a big sneeze. "A . . . TISHOO!"

The frill round the bottom of the bed shook. Red Riding Hood lifted it up to peep underneath. There was Grandma, safe and sound.

"Oh, Grandma!" she cried. "How clever you are!"

When Grandma was back in her bed, Red Riding Hood found her a clean nightcap. They were all very happy – all laughing and talking together.

"I feel better," said Grandma. "Let's have a party!"

And they did. Lovely brown eggs, with fresh bread and butter, and golden honey. One woodcutter went to fetch Red Riding Hood's mother. They all had a happy time. The squirrel sprang from branch to branch and all the birds sang louder and louder.

Jasper's Travels

"It should be lunch time by now," said Jasper the goldfish. He knew his friend Peter wasn't usually late feeding him, but it got rather boring sometimes just swimming round and round.

Jasper peered through the side of his bowl, and blinked crossly. He could see Peter and his mother and father eating their lunch.

"Just waiting and waiting," he went on. "I wish I could have a real adventure, but I have nowhere to go and nothing to do."

Just then Jasper felt his bowl being lifted high into the air, and carried along rather jerkily until he landed right next to the kitchen sink.

"Oh," gasped Jasper. "I suppose I've got to have my water changed now. I do hope the water is warm enough this time. Last week it was freezing. I had a chill for days – brrrr. Oh dear, and all this before lunch."

Peter was always very careful when he changed Jasper's water. He caught him first in a little fishing net, and popped him into a clean jar of water. Then he cleaned his bowl thoroughly and filled it with fresh water. Catching Jasper again in the little net, Peter carefully put him back into his bowl.

"My, that feels good," said Jasper and gave a wriggle of delight. "That feels very good," he said, and gave an even bigger wriggle.

Suddenly, with a jerk of his head, and with a flip of his tail, he jumped up and over the edge of his bowl, and into the sink. He wriggled towards a large round hole, and felt himself falling down, down, down. It was very dark.

"I must find some water soon," gasped Jasper.

Suddenly Jasper felt himself falling through into the bluest, cleanest water he had ever seen. All round him were beautiful plants and flowers, shells and stones, and tiny insects and grubs. Just then, a large grey fish with red spots swam by.

"Hello!" he called. "My name is Mr Plaice. Who are you?"

"I'm Jasper the goldfish," Jasper replied. "I'm lost. Where am I, please?"

"Why," replied Mr Plaice, "you're in the sea of course. We don't get many goldfish in the sea. You'd better watch out for sharks and the whales. They're very large, and would find you very tasty."

Jasper shuddered. He didn't like the idea of being eaten for supper. He thought only people did that.

"Come with me," said Mr Plaice. "I'll take care of you."

Together they swam through the clear waters until they
reached a large wooden object stuck in the sea bed.

"This is Fishville Colony," said Mr Plaice. "A large ship sank
here many years ago, and we've made it our home. It gives us
shelter when the sea is stormy and we can hide here safely if we
know there is any danger around."

All around swam the most beautiful fish Jasper had ever seen.
Baby minnows darted swiftly between plants, and swam in and
out of the timbers of the old ship. Everywhere he looked were fish of
different shapes and sizes.

Jasper swam up and up, nibbling as he went at any small insects which came within his reach. A big round object with two large eyes and eight spindly legs floated towards him.

"Who are you?" gasped Jasper.

"I'm Octopus," replied the odd shape. "I need all my legs for catching my food as I cannot swim around as quickly as you can."

Jasper quickly darted away and swam on further.

Suddenly, Jasper felt himself being dragged forward. All around him now were lots of other fish all trying in vain to swim free. He felt himself being pulled up and up until, once again, he was without water. This time he was packed between a shoal of heaving and wriggling fish. He could hear voices, men's voices.

"Not a bad catch this time."

The fishermen heaved the net into the boat and looked over their catch.

"Why," said one, "if it isn't a goldfish! Never caught one of those before. Better put him back into the sea."

"No, wait," said another voice. "I'll take him to my brother's pet store. A fine looking fish like that should fetch a good price."

Jasper felt himself being plunged into a box of icy water, and the little fishing boat rocked from side to side making Jasper feel rather queer.

"Oh dear," he said. "Whoever heard of a goldfish feeling seasick."

Soon the fishing boat was tied up, and the fisherman tucked the box under his arm.

Jasper closed his eyes sadly. How he longed to see his friend Peter again.

Inside the pet store the fisherman's brother looked down at Jasper. "Ah yes, I'll soon sell this little fellow. Let me put him into the tank with the other goldfish."

Once again, Jasper felt himself sliding into different waters, only this time into a tank already overcrowded with tiny fish.

"Mind your manners," snapped a little goldfish with silver lines on his back, as Jasper bumped into him for the third time.

"I'm sorry," replied Jasper, "but I'm looking for some food. It seems ages since I last ate, and I'm very hungry."

"We've eaten it all," came the reply. "We never get enough in here. Too many fish and not enough food. That's the trouble here."

Jasper suddenly became aware of a man peering into the tank looking at all the fish one by one.

"I expect he likes me the best," thought Jasper excitedly, and darted and swam as cleverly as he could.

"Yes, I'll take the lot," said the man to the store owner. He handed over some money, and lifted the tank up. He carried it out of the store and put the tank in the back of a large red truck. Off they went, all the fish bumping into each other as the truck rounded corners, until they arrived at a large park.

"Roll up, roll up. Lots of fun and games for everyone."

Jasper heard lots of shouting as the tank was lifted out and on to the centre of a large round stall. He opened his eyes wide. All around, people were throwing hoops trying to catch them on hooks in front of the tank. Some of the hooks had numbers on them.

"Come and play Hoop-la," shouted the man. "Win a beautiful goldfish."

Jasper had never been to a fairground before, and didn't like it very much at all. He felt very lonely and afraid.

Just then, he heard a voice shout, "Oh, I've won! I've won a goldfish!"

"Well done, Peter," a voice replied. "Now choose which one you would like."

Jasper gave the biggest wriggle he could manage. He *knew* that voice. It was his friend Peter.

"Why, this one looks just like Jasper," exclaimed Peter. "Wait! It *is* Jasper. Look, he's so excited he's trying to tell me to choose him. Hello, Jasper old fellow, we'll soon have you home safe again."

Peter just couldn't understand how Jasper had arrived at the fairground. He'd felt very upset when he had lost him, and never expected to see him again.

A man put Jasper into a little bag with airholes in the top, and Peter carried him home. On the table where Jasper's bowl had stood there was the biggest, shiniest fish tank he had ever seen.

"There," said Peter. "We bought this for you just before you disappeared. I shall put plants and rocks in it for you, and you'll be able to have much more fun."

Jasper smiled to himself as he swam through the clear water in his lovely new tank. It was wonderful to feel cosy and safe again and to have lots of food. As for his adventures, well, even a goldfish can dream sometimes.

The Hare and the Tortoise

A hare came leaping across the field. He loved darting this way and that, stopping to look and listen, then to be off again as fast as he could go.

He was at the hedge, nosing his way through into a grassy lane when he saw the tortoise. Hare sat up on his strong hind legs, ears held high and his whiskers twitching. He always laughed at Tortoise – that heavy shell, the funny wrinkled face and neck poking out in front, and those bent legs! . . . How could anyone walk on such legs?

"Poor old Tortoise," he chuckled. "He is so slow . . . slow as a snail!"

Then he called: "Hello there, Tortoise! . . . Are you walking your slowest or your fastest?"

"Always at the same pace, Hare," the tortoise replied. "Just slow but sure."

"There's one thing for sure," teased the hare, "you'll always be the last getting there – wherever it might be!"

"Oh, I don't know," Tortoise answered in his calm, thoughtful way. "I think we should have a race. I will win of course."

This amused the hare so much he was quite doubled up with laughter. "Do you . . . mean that?" he choked, trying to take a deep breath.

"Of course! I always mean what I say," said the tortoise.

A fox was peeping from behind a tree, listening and grinning with delight at what he heard. 'This will be fun,' he thought and came forward hoping to take part in some way.

"Good morning, gentlemen! . . . Can I help? . . . Get things going, perhaps?" he asked.

All the woodland animals stood by chatting and waiting to see the race.

When they'd agreed on how far to go and which tree should be the winning post, the hare and the tortoise stood ready at the starting line.

Fox gave the signal . . . They were off!

The hare bounded away and reached the top of the next hill in no time at all. There he stopped to look back.

"Poor old Tortoise," he said to himself, "not even in sight . . . Beat me indeed! . . . I might as well have a rest."

So, he settled down in the cool grass and fell fast asleep.

Meanwhile, the tortoise plodded on; step by step, never looking round, never stopping. He just kept doing what he'd made up his mind to do. Fox saw it all and smiled.

The other animals took the short cut across the field and were there at the post to watch for the winner.

It was a very hot day. The sun began to burn the hare's nose and so he woke up. The fox, waiting behind the hedge, turned and made a dash for the finishing line.

Hare sat up, rubbing his eyes, wondering what he was doing there.

"Oh yes, of course, the race," he mumbled. "Where's poor old Tortoise now?" and he glanced down the lane. There was no sign of those funny little legs. Hare looked the other way; the lane was empty.

"Ah well, I'd better push on . . . I'll give him a wave as I pass," and Hare giggled to think of it.

There was the winning post round the next bend, and everybody was jumping up and down with excitement.

'How nice!' Hare thought. 'My friends have come to cheer me.' Then he heard the words, "Come on Tortoise . . . Only a few steps . . . That's it! . . . You've WON . . . Good old Tortoise!"

Hare arrived feeling very foolish.

"How did you manage it, Tortoise?" everyone was asking.

"Well, slow and steady wins the race," he replied and started nibbling a juicy leaf.

I don't think Hare teased him any more – do you?

Icy Fingers

Once long ago, a farmer and his wife lived on the edge of the forest. They had one daughter who was very spoilt by her mother. She sat all day by the fire, combing her long hair while the servant girl did all the work. The servant girl worked from dawn till dusk, caring for the animals and working in the fields but she never complained.

One day, the farmer's wife shouted at her, saying "I cannot bear the sight of you any longer. Go out into the fields and never come back! I will not have you here any more."

The farmer begged his wife not to be so cruel as it was wintertime and snow lay deep on the ground, but nothing would make her change her mind. Out into the cold the girl went sad and forlorn. Who could she turn to for help . . . where could she go?

She sat down under a fir tree and began to cry. Suddenly she heard a faint sound. It was Jack Frost, king of ice and snow, jumping from tree to tree, cracking his fingers as he went.

He stopped and said to her, "Do you know who I am?"

The girl trembling with cold, said in a low voice, "Yes, you are Jack Frost. Have you come to take me with you?"

"Are you warm?" he asked, as she shivered in the wind.

"Quite warm," she replied, her breath like a film of ice on her lips.

He bent over and asked her once again, "Are you warm?"

The poor girl was so cold she could just gasp, "Still warm, but very frightened."

Jack Frost was so touched by her courage that his heart melted and he could not torment her any longer. He wrapped her in warm furs and sparkling jewels and lifted her into his sledge drawn by six white horses.

Back in the farm the mother and her daughter were sitting by the fire when all of a sudden, the door flew open and there stood the servant girl, dazzling in her jewels and furs.

The farmer's wife was so angry that she said to her daughter, "Stop combing your hair. Go out into the fields, sit in the same place and maybe the same thing will happen to you."

In a little while, Jack Frost came by and found the girl sitting by a tree and said to her, "Are you warm?"

"How stupid you are," she said. "Look at my hands and feet and see how cold they are!"

Then Jack Frost was so cross that he started to question her again and again. She was so rude to him that at last, he became very angry and froze her instantly into a large icicle.

While Jack Frost was casting his spell over the girl, the door of the farm blew open and her mother was caught in an icy blast. So she too, was frozen forever.

The Magic Porridge Pot

Once, there was a girl who lived with her mother in a tiny house on the outskirts of a small town. They were very poor and sometimes they were very hungry. Often they had nothing to eat at all.

One day, when the girl was out in the woods looking for mushrooms and blackberries, she met an old woman who was carrying an empty iron pot.

"Take it," said the old woman. She put the pot into the girl's hands. "Whenever you are hungry, say to it, 'Little pot, boil'. When you have enough, say, 'Little pot, stop'."

The girl thought it very strange, but she took the pot home and told her mother what the old woman had said.

"Put the pot on the table, say the words and we shall see what happens," said her mother.

"Little pot, boil," said the girl. As soon as she spoke, the pot began to bubble and hiss and steam began to rise from it.

"It's filling up," gasped the girl.

"It is truly a magic pot," said her mother. "Stop it, before it overflows."

"Little pot, stop," said the girl. The bubbling and hissing stopped at once. "What a lovely smell," she said.

"That looks and smells like porridge to me," said her mother. "Bring two plates and two spoons and we will taste it."

It was the sweetest, creamiest, nicest porridge they had ever tasted. With a magic porridge pot like that, their days of being hungry were over. It did not matter how much porridge they ate, there was always more to be had when they said the magic words, 'Little pot, boil'.

One day, when the girl was out, her mother set the pot on the table and said, "Little pot, boil." The bubbling began, the steam began to rise and the lovely smell of porridge filled the room. The sweet, creamy porridge reached the top of the pot. The girl's mother opened her mouth to say the words to stop the pot, but she could not remember them. All she could think of to say was "Um, er . . . that's enough." A tiny trickle of porridge began to run down the outside of the porridge pot. That had never happened before.

"Stop . . . stop . . . !" she cried. "I don't want any more . . . Stop filling up . . . Oh dear, oh dear . . . " She just could not remember the right words.

The pot bubbled and bubbled. The trickle of porridge became a stream. It spread across the table and fell in a sticky mess to the floor.

"Whatever shall I do?" she cried as she climbed on to a chair.

The pool of porridge spread to the door and outside along the street.

"Stop! . . . Stop! . . . " she shouted. "Come back porridge, get back into the pot . . . please stop!" The porridge took no notice. It would only stop if the right words were spoken. What were the right words?

"What is happening?" cried the people in the town. They took off their shoes and waded through the sticky mess.

"It's the pot . . . it will not stop," cried the girl's mother.

The dogs began to bark, the cats began to howl and everyone began to shout at the porridge pot.

"Stop making porridge before we all drown . . . Stop! Stop!"

The sweet, creamy porridge became like an overflowing river. It ran on and on, through the streets, into all the houses and the dog kennels. It filled up the fish ponds and the drains.

The girl was at her uncle's house on the other side of the town. She heard the noise outside and looked out of the window to see what was happening. As soon as she saw the river of porridge oozing through the streets, she knew just what to do. She ran home as fast as she could, through the sticky porridge.

When she came to the house, her mother was still shouting at the pot. "Stop cooking . . . stop bubbling . . . Stop! . . . Stop! . . . "

"Little pot, stop," said the girl. Those were the magic words and the pot did stop instantly.

"I will only use the pot in future when you are here," said the girl's mother. "I don't want that to happen again."

It took many days to clean up the mess because the porridge had stuck to everything. Perhaps it was not a good thing after all, to have a magic porridge pot.

Hidden Magic

One morning, when the mist was lying over the hills and the air was crisp and chilly, John the Ploughman took his plough from the barn and walked to a field that was overgrown with grass and tall weeds.

He enjoyed ploughing. He liked watching as the plough turned the earth and cut brown furrows that were as straight and true as lines ruled on paper with a ruler.

As the sun rose higher in the sky the mist cleared. It was going to be a fine day. John the Ploughman whistled along with the birds and was happy in his work.

He had reached the halfway mark and was turning his plough, when he thought he heard a strange sound. His ears were used to outdoor noises. Anything, even slightly unusual, caught his attention at once. He stood still and listened intently. The birds were singing in the hedgerow, the mice were scurrying in the undergrowth, the breeze was whispering in the leaves . . . but there WAS something else. It was very faint . . . but there it was again.

"I can hear someone crying," he said to a blackbird sitting on a branch.

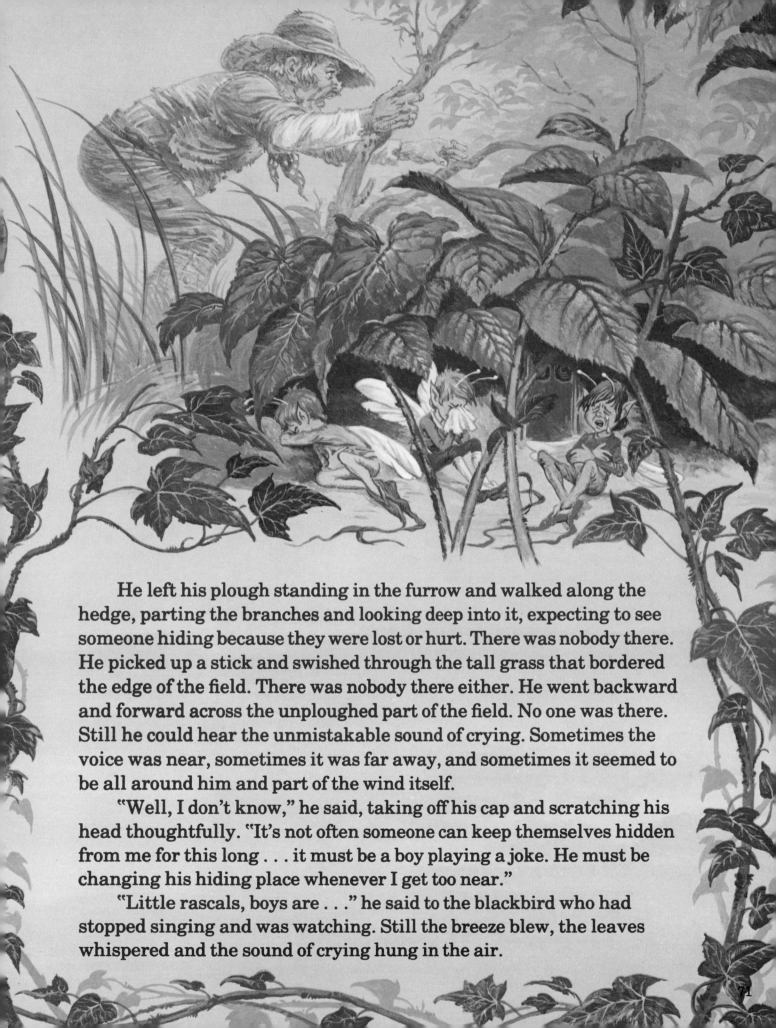

He left his plough standing in the furrow and walked along the hedge, parting the branches and looking deep into it, expecting to see someone hiding because they were lost or hurt. There was nobody there. He picked up a stick and swished through the tall grass that bordered the edge of the field. There was nobody there either. He went backward and forward across the unploughed part of the field. No one was there. Still he could hear the unmistakable sound of crying. Sometimes the voice was near, sometimes it was far away, and sometimes it seemed to be all around him and part of the wind itself.

"Well, I don't know," he said, taking off his cap and scratching his head thoughtfully. "It's not often someone can keep themselves hidden from me for this long . . . it must be a boy playing a joke. He must be changing his hiding place whenever I get too near."

"Little rascals, boys are . . ." he said to the blackbird who had stopped singing and was watching. Still the breeze blew, the leaves whispered and the sound of crying hung in the air.

71

John the Ploughman was about to admit that he had been beaten in a game of hide-and-seek by a boy, when he saw something lying on a flat stone close by the bottom of the hedge. It was a tiny shovel with a long handle. Picking it up carefully, John saw at once that the handle had been broken making it impossible to use.

"Ah, now I understand," said John softly. "The boy who is crying and hiding at the same time isn't playing a joke after all . . . he wants me to mend his shovel and is too shy to ask . . . boys are funny."

John cut a straight twig from the hedge with his pocket knife and stripped the bark from it. It only took him a few minutes to make it into a new handle for the shovel.

"Well," he said, when he had finished. "Are you coming to get it now that it is mended?"

Strangely the crying had stopped. He waited expectantly. But nobody came.

"I can't wait here all day. I have work to do," he said at last. "I know you are there somewhere, so I'll leave the shovel here on the stone where I found it. Perhaps you'll come and get it when I have gone." Off John went, shaking his head and thinking how sad it was for a boy to be THAT shy.

By evening the ploughing was finished. John looked with satisfaction at the neatly turned furrows.

"Looks like a bed with a brown corduroy cover," he said. "Good enough to sleep in."

As John walked home along the edge of the field he wondered if the boy had come back for his shovel.

"I'll go round by the hedgerow," he said. "It won't take any longer and then I'll know for sure."

When he came to the stone where he had laid the shovel he saw at once that it had gone. To his surprise, lying in the same place on the same stone, was a tiny loaf of bread.

It smelled so delicious that he couldn't resist popping it into his mouth. He could not remember ever tasting anything so marvellous before.

As John walked home, still with the taste of the bread in his mouth, he thought to himself, 'Perhaps it wasn't a boy I heard crying after all . . . perhaps . . . but no, of course it couldn't have been . . .'

But thinking about everything that had happened that day, he wondered all the same.

As well he might, for the field he had ploughed that day lay like a roof over a fairy village. The shovel he had found was used every day by the fairy baker to lift the hot bread, pies and beautiful cakes as light as thistledown out of the oven. Once the shovel was broken everyone went hungry and the crying of the children was what John had heard.

Now all was well. The children were happy and the baker was hard at work again. John still wondered about the little shovel with a long handle and the little loaf he found every Spring when he came to plough the field once more.

Pixie Visitors

Pixies enjoy getting together and having fun.
The trouble with pixies is, they always hold their
parties at night when ordinary people are trying
to sleep.

Once, there was a farmer and his wife. They
had no one to help them on the farm and were always
very tired at the end of the day. When the last
chore was done they would put an extra log on the
fire to keep it glowing through the night and go
straight to bed.

One cold dark night, when there was frost on
the hedgerow and icicles hanging from the roof, a
pixie face peeped through the farmhouse window.
The pixie took one look at the empty kitchen and
the glowing fire and sent out a message. Before
many minutes had passed the farmhouse kitchen was
as crowded with pixies as a railway station is
crowded with people in the rush hour.

It wouldn't have mattered if the pixies had
had their fun quietly. But they didn't. Having
fun to a pixie means squealing and shouting and
screeching and singing. It means rattling and
banging and slamming and clanking and popping.
It means stamping and clapping. It means making
a HULLABALOO!!! No one can sleep through it.
Not even a tired farmer and his tired wife.

"Who is making all that noise?" cried the farmer's wife, sitting up in bed and pressing her hands to her ears.

"There are pixies playing in the kitchen," said the farmer who was on his hands and knees peeping through a hole in the floor.

"Then tell them to go and play somewhere else," grumbled his wife.

"I can't do that," said the farmer. And he was right! He couldn't! If he offended the pixies there was no telling what they might do. There are so many things on a farm that a pixie can make go wrong. They can curdle the milk and stop the hens laying for a start. If they are really annoyed they can make EVERYTHING go wrong.

"We'll just have to put up with the noise," sighed the farmer.

The farmhouse kitchen was warm and cosy and the pixies liked it so much they began to come EVERY night. The farmer and his wife hardly slept at all. They grew more and more tired. They just couldn't stop yawning during the day. When the farmer's wife fell asleep in the hen house and dropped all the eggs she had been collecting, the farmer decided the time had come to do something. But what? Offend the pixies and they were in trouble.

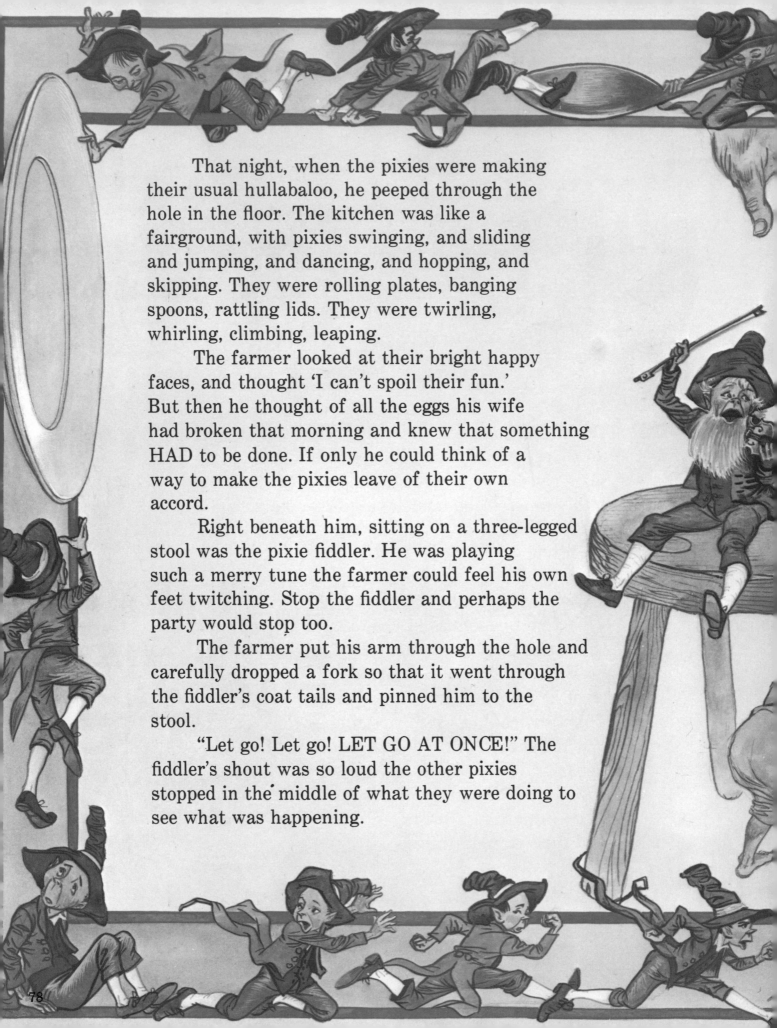

That night, when the pixies were making their usual hullabaloo, he peeped through the hole in the floor. The kitchen was like a fairground, with pixies swinging, and sliding and jumping, and dancing, and hopping, and skipping. They were rolling plates, banging spoons, rattling lids. They were twirling, whirling, climbing, leaping.

The farmer looked at their bright happy faces, and thought 'I can't spoil their fun.' But then he thought of all the eggs his wife had broken that morning and knew that something HAD to be done. If only he could think of a way to make the pixies leave of their own accord.

Right beneath him, sitting on a three-legged stool was the pixie fiddler. He was playing such a merry tune the farmer could feel his own feet twitching. Stop the fiddler and perhaps the party would stop too.

The farmer put his arm through the hole and carefully dropped a fork so that it went through the fiddler's coat tails and pinned him to the stool.

"Let go! Let go! LET GO AT ONCE!" The fiddler's shout was so loud the other pixies stopped in the middle of what they were doing to see what was happening.

"A giant! A GIANT!" they shrieked when they saw the arm coming through the hole in the ceiling. (To them it WAS a giant sized arm).

"A GIANT COME TO PUT US ALL IN A PIE!" they shrieked when they saw the fork.

They were so frightened they made themselves as small as flies and flew in a swarm through the keyhole. They were gone in a twinkling of an eye. The kitchen was empty. Well, almost.

The fiddler had made himself small too, but the fork was still pinning his coat tails to the stool, and try though he might he could NOT make the stool shrink. An ordinary sized stool will NOT go through a keyhole. It doesn't matter how hard it is pushed or pulled.

The farmer did not want the fiddler to hurt himself so he ran downstairs in his nightshirt and pulled the fork from his coat tails. The stool fell to the floor with a clatter and the fiddler and his fiddle shot through the keyhole like an arrow from a crossbow.

Whishshshshshshs . . . . he went, into the night.

The pixies never came back to the farmhouse. They found somewhere safer to hold their parties and the farmer and his wife were able to get to sleep at night.

The Gingerbread Man

A little old man and a little old woman lived in a tiny cottage. Every day was the same, because they had no children to play with or to make them laugh.

One day, the little old woman had an idea. It was such a splendid idea, she had to sit down and think about it. The little old man was sitting outside in the sun, so the little old woman said to herself, "I will make a little gingerbread man!"

She started mixing things: fat, sugar, and eggs; then flour and ginger. She put in lots of ginger and made him a lovely dark brown. She rolled the dough and cut out the shape of a little man.

"Now, currants for his eyes and his buttons. Some lemon peel for his nose and his mouth . . . That's fine!"

She slid the gingerbread on to a baking sheet and put it into the oven to bake.

Later that morning, the little old woman heard a voice. "Let me out! . . . Let me out!"

The voice came from the oven! Very carefully, she peeped inside. The Gingerbread Man leapt out!

"Wait!" she called. "Come back!" But he was off and running fast.

"Don't just sit there, little old man!" she cried. "Help me catch him!"

They ran after him. "Stop! Stop!" they shouted.

The Gingerbread Man grinned and called,

"Run, run as fast as you can.
You can't catch me
I'm the Gingerbread Man."
And they couldn't!

A cow stood across his path. The Gingerbread Man ran between its legs.

"Mmm-ind your manners!" she mooed. "What are you doing?"

"I am running away!" laughed the Gingerbread Man. "I have run away from the little old woman and the little old man, so I am running away from you!

Run, run as fast as you can.
You can't catch me
I'm the Gingerbread Man."
He was right. The cow could not catch him!

He raced past a horse
trotting through a gate.

"Whoa!" called the horse.
"Wait for me!"

"Are you running away too?"
cried the Gingerbread Man.

"Why not? . . . Hee—hee—ee!"
neighed the horse. "The gate's
open."

"I run away from
everybody!" said the Gingerbread
Man. "I will run away from you
too!

Run, run as fast as you can.
You can't catch me
I'm the Gingerbread Man."

And even at a gallop the
horse couldn't catch him.

Round the next bend he met a fox.

"Hello!" called the fox. "Why, you are brown, just like me . . .
Look, we make a good pair."

The Gingerbread Man didn't stop. He ran faster and faster,
calling out, "I've run away from the little old woman, the little old
man, a cow AND a horse, so I can run away from you!

Run, run as fast as you can.
You can't catch me
I'm the Gingerbread Man."

But . . .

At last he stopped on the edge of a river.

"Oh!" said the Gingerbread Man, "I shall get wet . . . What can
I do?"

Up came the fox.

"You can sit on my tail, little brown friend. We will cross the river in no time."

So the Gingerbread Man climbed on to the fox's tail.

Soon the fox said, "Little friend, you will get wet on my tail. Jump on my back."

So the Gingerbread Man jumped on to the fox's back.

Half-way across the river the fox said, "Little friend, you are too heavy. Jump on my nose . . . You will be able to see better."

The Gingerbread Man laughed and jumped on to the fox's nose.

"This is fun," he said.

When the fox had nearly reached the other side, he tossed his head. Up went the Gingerbread Man, spinning over and over in the air. Then . . . snap! snap! He was caught!

The fox gobbled him up and that was the end of the Gingerbread Man.

Mother Holle

Once there were two step-sisters, who were as different as chalk and cheese. Martha was idle and never did a thing unless she HAD to, which wasn't very often for she was her mother's favourite. Anna was always busy. She HAD to be, for she was only a step-daughter.

One day, Anna was sitting in the garden spinning when she pricked her finger. A speck of blood fell onto the shuttle. She was trying to wash it clean when it slipped from her fingers and fell to the bottom of the well.

"YOU dropped it! YOU must go down and get it!" shouted her step-mother in such a rage that Anna had no choice but to do as she was told. She must have bumped her head as she fell, for she remembered nothing until she woke, and found herself in a pleasant field. She got to her feet and began to walk. Presently she came to an oven.

"Take me out . . . before I burn," **cried** the bread in the oven.

Anna took the bread from the oven and set it to cool.

A little further on she came to a tree.

"Shake me!" cried the tree. "My apples are ripe!"

Anna shook the tree. When all the apples had fallen she piled them **neatly**, then went on her way until she came to the house of a witch.

"You must come and work for me," said the witch. "Your most important task will be to shake my feather bed every morning. I am Mother Holle. If my bed is not shaken properly there will be no snow."

Mother Holle was very kind to Anna and for a while Anna was happy, but then she began to feel homesick.

"You have worked very hard," said Mother Holle, "and I will show you the way home." She took Anna to a hidden door. "Go through," said Mother Holle, handing her the lost shuttle. As Anna stepped through the door a shower of golden rain fell all about her and clung to her hair and her clothes.

"The gold is yours," said Mother Holle. "Goodbye my dear."

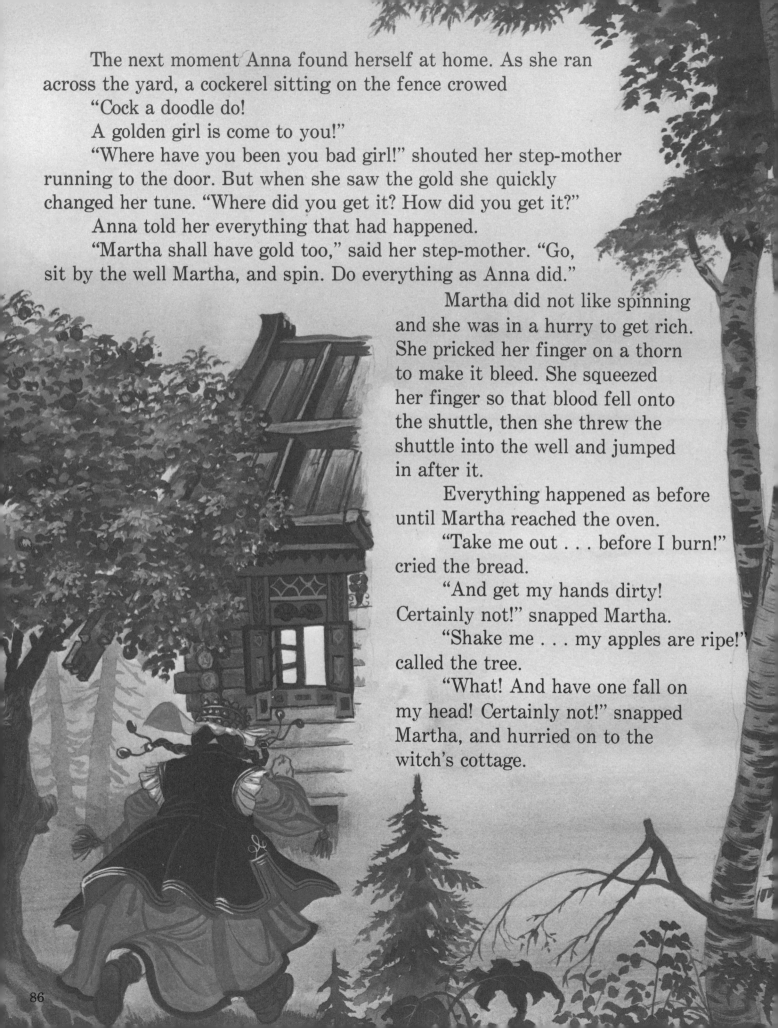

The next moment Anna found herself at home. As she ran across the yard, a cockerel sitting on the fence crowed

"Cock a doodle do!

A golden girl is come to you!"

"Where have you been you bad girl!" shouted her step-mother running to the door. But when she saw the gold she quickly changed her tune. "Where did you get it? How did you get it?"

Anna told her everything that had happened.

"Martha shall have gold too," said her step-mother. "Go, sit by the well Martha, and spin. Do everything as Anna did."

Martha did not like spinning and she was in a hurry to get rich. She pricked her finger on a thorn to make it bleed. She squeezed her finger so that blood fell onto the shuttle, then she threw the shuttle into the well and jumped in after it.

Everything happened as before until Martha reached the oven.

"Take me out . . . before I burn!" cried the bread.

"And get my hands dirty! Certainly not!" snapped Martha.

"Shake me . . . my apples are ripe!" called the tree.

"What! And have one fall on my head! Certainly not!" snapped Martha, and hurried on to the witch's cottage.

"I will come and work for you," she said to Mother Holle, without waiting to be asked.

On the first day she worked well. On the second day she swept the dust under the hearth-rug and didn't bother to shake Mother Holle's mattress at all. On the third day she stayed in bed until mid-afternoon.

"It is time for you to go home," said Mother Holle.

"You must pay me first," said Martha greedily.

"Certainly, I will pay you," said Mother Holle, and led her to the hidden door. This time, instead of a shower of gold descending like rain, a shower of black pitch came pouring down. It covered Martha from head to foot. It was horrid!

"That is just payment for the work you have done," said Mother Holle sternly, and closed the door behind her.

When Martha ran sobbing across the yard to the house, the cockerel sitting on the fence crowed,

"Cock a doodle do!
A dirty girl is come to you!"

The Piglet and the Gnome

One night a thief stole a fat little piglet and put him in a sack.

The piglet squealed as he was carried away, but the sack muffled the sound of the piglet's voice and his master did not hear him.

The piglet was heavy and the thief had a long way to walk. After a while he decided to take a rest. He put the sack on the ground, then sat on the ground himself and leant against a tree. He didn't mean to go to sleep, but he made the mistake of closing his eyes, and before many minutes had passed he was snoring.

The fat little piglet did not like being in the sack. He squealed and fidgeted and wriggled. He huffed and he puffed and he squirmed. Now it so happened that the thief had put the sack right near a hole where a gnome had his house. The gnome was nearly deafened when the piglet squealed, and nearly tipped out of bed by all the fidgeting and wriggling. He went outside to see what was causing the disturbance.

He untied the sack and looked inside.

"Hallo," he said. "What are you doing in there?"

"I've been stolen," said the piglet. "I don't like it in here. I want to go home."

"And so you shall," said the gnome who could understand pig talk perfectly well. He helped the piglet out of the sack and sent him on his way.

Then, because he liked having a bit of fun, the gnome got into the sack himself and waited for the thief to wake up, which he did, a little while later.

The thief hoisted the sack onto his shoulder and set off along a dark lane. He whistled to himself, and thought about all the things he could do with the piglet he had in his sack.

There was another gnome sitting in one of the trees in the lane. He was a friend of the gnome in the sack. He knew his friend was about because he had heard him talking to the piglet, but he couldn't see him.

"Where are you Dick?" he called.

The thief nearly jumped out of his skin. He looked all around. There was no sign of anyone, that he could see. 'I must be imagining things,' he thought. And then, before he had recovered from his fright, he heard another voice. A voice that came from just behind his right ear.

> "I'm in the sack
> Riding pig-a-back!"

The thief felt his hair stand on end. He thought the piglet was still in the sack. After all, hadn't he put it there himself? He dropped the sack. . .and he ran. He wanted nothing to do with a talking piglet. It would tell the whole world it had been stolen and who had stolen it.

"There goes someone who will never dare to steal another piglet," laughed the gnomes as the thief disappeared into the distance.

The Little Shoemakers

Two little leprechauns known as Larry and Tack had their home deep in a forest on the side of a hill, in the 'Land of Joy'.

Of course, there were lots of other little people living there in what could be described as a village, but Larry and Tack were the most important, by far. Being expert boot and shoemakers they hardly ever had an idle moment.

"Do you not think, Larry, that it's time we opened a factory?" asked Tack one day when they were busier than usual.

"I was thinking the same thing myself," replied Larry.

"We'll have to train some young fellows to do the job," said Tack.

And so the factory was opened. It was built of hundreds of toadstools, quite unlike a work place for grown-up people.

Lessons in shoemaking were given to young leprechauns who had left school and were clever with their hands. All day long these little men sat cross-legged on their toadstools, hammering, shaping and stitching.

Boots for wearing in the daytime were of acorn and walnut shells lined with thistledown. Most of these were for the fairies who also lived in the forest and were great friends of Larry and Tack. Slippers for dancing were made of flower petals, stitched with cobweb thread and trimmed with bluebells, that tinkled with every step.

News of this wonderful factory reached the ears of Queen Maeve who paid a visit. So pleased was the Queen with such good work that she ordered ten pairs of shoes and ten pairs of slippers.

So Larry and Tack became shoemakers by Royal Appointment to Her Majesty.

Stories of the factory spread North, South, East and West, and the place was like a beehive with everyone working hard. The squirrels collected acorn shells, the rabbits scurried here and there gathering special rushes for stitching and the wood pigeons flew back and forth with thistledown and wool from the backs of sheep in their beaks. It was such a happy place. Everyone was working. Nobody grumbled and the customers came back again and again.

Indeed, children, if you crept silently to the edge of the forest and listened carefully, you might hear faint hammering and rustling as the little fellows worked away.

Then one day, Larry and Tack had the shock of their lives. Sally Swallow, the post, flew in with a letter.

It was from Giant Grumplelumpkin. He had come to the 'Land of Joy' on a visit to his cousin Giant Funnybones. They hadn't seen each other for ten years.

Before long, Grumplelumpkin heard about the factory.

"Just what I want," he told his cousin. "I'm taking a walk around the world and I want a fine, strong pair of boots. I'll write them a letter."

Poor little Larry and Tack were very, very frightened when the letter came. They had never seen a giant, much less his feet.

They had heard that giants were very, very large and often quite nasty fellows, with queer tastes in what they liked to eat.

All the fairies, birds and animals in the forest were terrified when they were told that the giant was coming. So they held a meeting at the factory to find out if anyone could think of a bright idea.

"I know," piped up little Thumper Rabbit. "I know where there are heaps of boxes, plastic boxes. I know too, that real people often wear plastic boots and shoes because they are so strong and hard to wear out. They are in a dump across the river if only we could get them," he gasped.

"You are a very kind and clever little fellow to think of that," said Larry. "It's a great idea, but how can we get them across?"

"No problem at all," chipped in Busy Billie Beaver. "I'll get the boxes for you both and be delighted to help."

That very evening Billie Beaver swam across the river. With his paws he rolled and pushed the boxes to the water's edge. Then the whole family of beavers came to help. Even the babies joined in the fun.

By morning there was a mountain of boxes, enough to make a dozen pairs of boots for the biggest giant in the world. Everyone felt happier now, but they still feared the visit of Giant Grumplelumpkin.

The next day came, and with it a peal of thunder. It wasn't thunder at all but the heavy footsteps of the giant himself coming down the hill. He was enormous, as high as the forest trees which he brushed out of his way with huge hands. He looked down at Larry and Tack who were shivering with fright, and he roared with laughter.

"I'll sit down," he bellowed as he slid down and rested his back against a tree, "and then you can measure my feet. Although I'm very big, I'm not very bad, you know, and I won't gobble you up, so you needn't be afraid."

He pulled off his big boots which had holes underneath from all the walking he had done.

Larry got busy measuring, and Tack writing down. They couldn't help but wink at each other when the giant wasn't looking. His big toe was nearly as long as themselves. The little animals hiding in the long grass nudged each other.

"That's that," said Larry, pretending to be very brave as he rolled up his measuring tape, though his legs were shaking.

"Mr Giant Grumplelumpkin, your boots will be ready in two days."

"Thank you," replied the giant who had quite good manners. "I can see you know your job," and off he strode, crashing through the trees and over the hill.

Now the work began in earnest. First the cutting of the boxes. Billie Beaver was very good at that. His teeth were so sharp that he had lots of boxes cut in no time.

"These boots must be perfect," said Larry as he set to work.

"Certainly we must keep up our good name," replied Tack.

So they cut and shaped and stitched and the best workers were allowed to make the white tops for the boots.

Everyone helped, and in two days the boots were ready. Very nice they looked too, in black and white shiny 'leather'.

Larry hung the boots from the branch of a tree and they all waited for Giant Grumplelumpkin to return.

Along he came, quite early and all smiles.

"Hello, friends," he said settling himself against the tree. Then he saw the boots. "They are fit for a king," he cried out, as he fitted them on. "What lovely soft lining and so cool. My feet won't hurt any more."

He walked round, delighted with himself, smiling broadly.

Then from his pocket he took two little golden hammers as presents for Larry and Tack.

Before turning to leave he asked, "May I come and visit you when I return from my travels?"

"Anytime, anytime," they all shouted back.

Then, little drops of rain began to fall. It really wasn't rain at all, but happy tears from the eyes of the gentle giant.

French Puck

French Puck was very fond of playing tricks. He never did anyone harm, but he sometimes made people feel very foolish.

One day he overheard two people talking.

"It is our wedding day a week from tomorrow," said Jeanne. "It is market day today. We must go into town and buy all the things we need to set up house."

"There will be a lot to carry," said Jules. "We must take the horse and cart."

French Puck chuckled to himself, and sat on a fence and teased some chickens to while away the time while he waited for their return. With so many things to buy they were sure to forget something.

It was late afternoon before Jeanne and Jules returned. The cart was so loaded there was barely room for them on it.

French Puck leapt through the air, light as a goose feather, and sat on a chair leg behind them.

"Have we knives?" Jeanne was asking.

"Yes."

"Have we soap?"

"Yes."

"Then we have everything we need," said Jeanne with a happy sigh, and she snuggled up to Jules and began to dream about their wedding day.

The horse was trotting. The birds were singing. Jules was whistling. Jeanne was dreaming. And French Puck was waiting. He didn't have long to wait.

Suddenly, Jeanne sat up with such a start, Jules jerked on the horse's reins, and between them they almost upset the cart.

"Oh, no," wailed Jeanne.

A gleeful grin spread across French Puck's face. He rubbed his hands together in anticipation and his pointed ears twitched.

'Ho, ho,' he thought to himself. 'She's remembered something she has forgotten.'

"Whatever made you shout out like that?" asked Jules when they had quietened the horse and made sure nothing had fallen from the cart.

"I've forgotten to buy the thread the dressmaker needs to sew my wedding clothes," sighed Jeanne.

"Is THAT all! Surely you've got thread at home," said Jules.

"Only white . . . I need pink, and the palest of yellow, and apricot and delicate sky blue, and one with a touch of green in it. We shall have to go back to town to get some."

Jules sighed. It was a long way back to town, but he supposed he would have to go. He had the cart turned half way across the road when Jeanne cried out again.

"Look! Look!"

"What now?" grumbled Jules, who had quite enough to do trying to persuade the horse to take the right direction.

"Hey! Be careful!" he cried as Jeanne jumped from the cart.

"Look! A ball of thread!" And what a ball of thread it was! It had ALL the colours in it that she needed -- pink, yellow, apricot, sky blue and delicate green.

"Oh, what a lucky thing I saw it," cried Jeanne.

"But how did it get there?" asked Jules.

"This isn't the time to be asking silly questions," said Jeanne, climbing back onto the cart.

Jules turned the cart homewards again and they continued on their way, with Jeanne carrying the precious ball of thread on her lap, and with French Puck doing somersaults on the chair leg behind them.

The dressmaker was very pleased when she saw the thread. "It's absolutely perfect," she said. She was even more pleased with it as she sewed the wedding clothes. It was as smooth as silk, it didn't break, it didn't knot, and each colour was exactly the right length.

The wedding day came, and everyone, and that included French
Puck, gathered outside the church to see the new bride. How
pretty she looked.

"What a beautiful dress!" everybody exclaimed.

And then it happened! Crick! Crack! The tiny coloured
bows decorating the skirt began to float to the ground.

"Ooh!" gasped Jeanne.

"What is happening?" gasped everyone else.

Crick! Crack! The muslin flowers decorating the bodice
fell in a shower of petals.

Crick! Crack! The frill round the bottom of the skirt fell to the ground . . . then the skirt itself tumbled round Jeanne's ankles . . . the sleeves came apart and fell from her arms . . . the bodice fell into five different pieces.

Poor Jeanne was left standing in her petticoat, with her wedding dress in tatters around her. Someone ran from the crowd and put a cloak round her shoulders, and Jules took her home so that she could put on another dress.

"The thread I sewed with must have been rotten," said the dressmaker, who was blushing as scarlet as Jeanne herself. Oh, the shame of it all.

When everyone else had gone, she gathered the pieces together. She looked at them very carefully. She turned each piece over and over. She couldn't find one tiny piece of sewing thread anywhere. It had ALL disappeared.

"I should have known such perfect thread was too good to be true," she sighed.

The mystery was never explained, but then nobody had seen French Puck, had they?

Little Red Hen

Little Red Hen strutted out of the farmyard and into Farmer Brown's big field. The wheat had been cut and gathered so she could scratch about anywhere.

"I might find some ears of wheat that the farmer's men have dropped," she clucked.

And she did. They were fine fat ones, full of golden grains. She carried them back to the farmyard to show her friends.

"Cluck, cluck!" called Little Red Hen. "Will you help me plant these grains?"

"Oh, No—o—!" yawned Ginger Cat. "I'm too sleee—py." Ginger Cat went up on to the roof of the barn and went to sleep.

"Oh, No—o—!" squeaked Grey Rat. "I am busy storing winter food in the barn." Grey Rat scampered away.

"Oh, No—o—!" grunted Pink Pig. "I am off to find some acorns." She trotted away into the trees.

"Very well," said Little Red Hen. "I will plant them myself."

And she did. She put them in straight rows. She watched the rows every day. She saw green shoots peeping up out of the ground. Then she saw the wheat at the top begin to ripen.

"My wheat is ready!" called Little Red Hen to the animals. "Will you help me gather it?"

"Not today," said Ginger Cat. "I must wash my fur."

"Don't count on me," squeaked Grey Rat. "My work is never done."

"You can see I'm too busy," grunted Pink Pig. "I have ten piglets to feed!"

"Very well," said Little Red Hen. "I will gather it myself."

And she did. She snipped each stalk and made a neat bundle.

"That's done!" she clucked. "Will you help me carry the wheat to the miller?"

"Impossible!" said Ginger Cat.

"Quite impossible!" squeaked Grey Rat.

"Quite, quite impossible!" grunted Pink Pig.

"Very well," said Little Red Hen, "I will carry it myself."

And she did. She carried it all the way to the mill. The great stones at the mill turned round, grinding the grains into flour. When the flour was fine enough, the miller put it into a linen bag.

"Thank you," said Little Red Hen.

When she came back to the farmyard, Little Red Hen called out, "Here is the flour . . . Who will help me take it to the baker to be made into bread?"

"Out of the question," said Ginger Cat, walking away.

"Quite out of the question," squeaked Grey Rat, running off.

"Quite, quite out of the question," grunted Pink Pig. "I am too fat to go anywhere."

"I suppose 'out of the question' means 'No'," said Little Red Hen. "I will take it myself."

And she did. She went to the baker and brought back a crusty loaf.

"Who will help me eat this lovely new bread?" she clucked.

The animals all gathered round. "I will!" said Ginger Cat, twitching his whiskers.

"So will I!" squeaked Grey Rat. "I am so hungry."

"Don't forget me!" grunted Pink Pig. "It looks delicious!"

"It is delicious," said Little Red Hen, "but you didn't help me at all . . . so it is quite out of the question for you to have any of it! Cluck! Cluck!"

Spotty Potty

Percy Potamus said "Oh whatamus
Am I going to do today?
On my tum there are some spotamus,
Not just a few but rather a lotamus.
In my bed I think I'll stay.
My head is aching, I feel hotamus,
Now I see there are spots on my poor
botamus!
Oh, I am a poorly Potamus,
Wish my spots would go away."

   His Mother Mrs Hippy Potamus
Said "German Measles is what you've
gotamus,
I'll bring your breakfast on a tray.

   Tomorrow those spots will be only
dotamus,
You'll feel better and want to play."

The Two Wizards

Once there were three brothers. The two eldest spent all their spare time playing draughts, and the youngest spent all his time learning how to become a wizard. One day, Bertram, who already knew a thing or two about wizardry, said, to his brothers,

"I feel like having some fun. I will change myself into a horse, and you can take me into the city and sell me."

"What will happen when you are sold?" asked his brothers.

"It will be fun to find out," said Bertram.

Who should buy Bertram in his new shape as a white horse, but the King himself. He paid for him with twelve of the best elephants in the palace elephant stable.

"What are you going to do?" whispered Bertram's brothers as the King prepared to mount. "The King will behead you if he finds out you have tricked him."

"Don't worry about me," whispered Bertram. "Take the elephants and go home."

The white horse gave the King a splendid ride. No one else could keep up with him. When they arrived at the palace gate the King had to dismount to open the gate himself.

No sooner had he dismounted than the white horse bolted.

"Catch that horse! Catch that horse!" shouted the King. But by the time the grooms had mounted their horses, the white horse was nowhere to be seen.

The King sent for his own wizard.

"I paid twelve of my best elephants for that horse," he said. "You MUST find it."

The King's wizard was no fool. He knew a thing or two himself. 'Set a horse to catch a horse,' he thought, and changed himself into a black stallion.

The white horse was grazing in a field. He heard the black stallion galloping towards him, and changed himself into a large white eagle. He soared up into the sky on strong white wings.

The King's wizard, who certainly did know a thing or two, changed into a black eagle. He soared up into the sky on strong black wings.

The white eagle saw him coming and changed into a white hawk. The black eagle changed into a black kite and chased the hawk into the trees, where Bertram's brothers were sitting playing draughts.

The white hawk changed into a white draught piece and hid amongst the other pieces on the board.

The black kite changed into the King's wizard.

"May I have my draught piece?" he asked.

"These are OUR draught pieces," said Bertram's brothers.

"Count them. You will find you have one too many," said the King's wizard. Of course, when Bertram's brothers counted the pieces, they found they did have one too many.

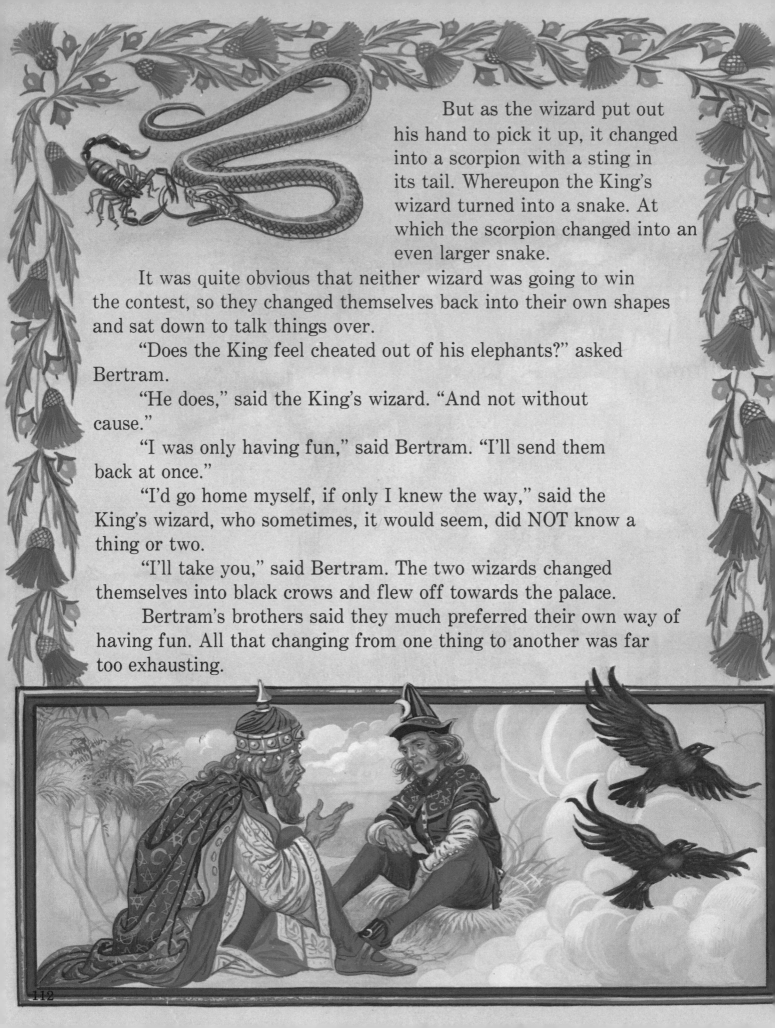

But as the wizard put out his hand to pick it up, it changed into a scorpion with a sting in its tail. Whereupon the King's wizard turned into a snake. At which the scorpion changed into an even larger snake.

It was quite obvious that neither wizard was going to win the contest, so they changed themselves back into their own shapes and sat down to talk things over.

"Does the King feel cheated out of his elephants?" asked Bertram.

"He does," said the King's wizard. "And not without cause."

"I was only having fun," said Bertram. "I'll send them back at once."

"I'd go home myself, if only I knew the way," said the King's wizard, who sometimes, it would seem, did NOT know a thing or two.

"I'll take you," said Bertram. The two wizards changed themselves into black crows and flew off towards the palace.

Bertram's brothers said they much preferred their own way of having fun. All that changing from one thing to another was far too exhausting.

The Firework Party

"I'm going to the fairy market to buy nice things to eat and drink while we watch the Sherbert's firework party tonight," said Esmeralda. "Will you come with me and carry the shopping home, Slibberslob?"

"No, I won't," said Slibberslob. "I want to go out to play. You can carry your silly shopping home yourself."

Slibberslob, the gnome, lived with Esmeralda in a bird-box at the bottom of Mr and Mrs Sherbert's garden. He was a naughty little gnome, and was sometimes very rude to people.

"Well," said Esmeralda, "mind you don't get into mischief while I'm away. It looks as if it might snow, so you could build a snowman if it does."

"I don't want to build a snowman," muttered Slibberslob. "I want to play tricks on somebody."

He chuckled as he watched Esmeralda hurry away with her basket. Already he had thought of some mischief he could get up to.

He fetched a watering-can and sprinkled water over Mrs Robin's babies to make them think it was raining.

Then he pulled all the leaves from Dozy Dormouse, who had gone to sleep for the winter.

Then he called "Fire! Fire!" in a loud voice down Roland Rabbit's burrow. He roared with laughter as all the little Rabbit children came scuttling out in alarm. He didn't laugh for long, though, because Grandpa Rabbit happened to be coming up from the railway station on a visit to the Rabbits. He saw what Slibberslob did. He was a big rabbit and very fierce. He carried a thick walking-stick, and he ran at Slibberslob, waving his stick and shouting angrily.

Slibberslob raced away, with Grandpa Rabbit after him.

Grandpa could run fast, and if Slibberslob hadn't noticed that Mr Sherbert's shed door was open a little way, he would have felt the weight of Grandpa Rabbit's stick on him. He hid behind the shed door until Grandpa Rabbit had given up searching for him. Then, just as he was about to go, he gave a cry of delight. "Fireworks!" he cried. Mr Sherbert had stored the fireworks he had bought for his children's firework party, in the shed.

"Ah!" chuckled Slibberslob. "Now I can have a firework party all to myself."

He decided to use one of the fireworks to play a trick on Mrs Owl, who lived in a tall tree not far from the bird-box. Mrs Owl slept all day and hunted at night, and she often scolded Slibberslob for making a noise and waking her up.

"I'll wake her up all right," Slibberslob said gleefully. "It will serve her right for going to sleep when other folk are awake. I'll take this rocket. It will rush right up past Mrs Owl's bedroom window. What a fright it will give her! Ha, ha, ha!"

He took a rocket out of Mr Sherbert's box and then found a box of matches. Peeping out to make sure that Grandpa Rabbit wasn't anywhere about, he crept out of the shed and hurried along to Mrs Owl's tree.

"Wouldn't it be fun if it sailed right through her bedroom window!" he laughed.

Slibberslob had never set off a firework before, and he thought he would hold the rocket in his hand. All children know that rockets are not safe. They must be fixed in the neck of a bottle so they will go straight up in the air. Slibberslob had never bothered to listen when told about this. When he lit the rocket there was a loud hissing noise. Suddenly, the rocket took off with a loud whoosh – with Slibberslob on the end of it.

The naughty gnome was too startled to let go and clung on tightly as the rocket soared away. It travelled at tremendous speed. It didn't go straight up in the air; it went in the direction Slibberslob held it, only a short distance above the ground.

Slibberslob couldn't guide it once it had taken off. It went straight on, through everything that stood in its way. Poor scared Slibberslob was whisked through a prickly hedge, then through Mrs Jackdaw's washing which was hanging on a line. Mr Jackdaw's white collar curled itself round Slibberslob's neck, and a sock twined about his leg. Straight across the highway flew the rocket, at a great pace. A big black crow was just about to land and nearly collided with Slibberslob. He was so annoyed that he gave Slibberslob a sharp peck as he passed.

"Ow!" yelled Slibberslob.

"Look where you're going!" croaked the crow after him. "You are a danger to traffic."

The rocket whooshed on, but presently began to lose speed, and just as it reached the fairy market it began to come down. It flew low through the open door of a bakehouse in the market, and plunged into a bag of flour in a corner. Slibberslob followed it head-first.

"Ow, I'm smothered!" wailed the gnome.

He struggled out of the bag, covered in flour from head to toe. The first person who saw him was Esmeralda, who had stepped into the bakehouse to buy buns.

"Why, Slibberslob," she cried, "you came after all to carry my shopping home! How kind of you! It's so heavy. Dear me, I didn't know it was snowing. You ought to have put on an overcoat; you're covered with snow. Never mind, I think it has stopped now."

Slibberslob couldn't say a word. Whether Esmeralda knew it was flour and not snow that covered him, he couldn't guess. He didn't care either. He didn't feel like explaining what had happened to him. Instead, he quietly picked up Esmeralda's shopping basket and trudged home with it. Esmeralda chattered happily by his side, and told him how much she was looking forward to the firework party, but Slibberslob only muttered to himself: "I don't care whether I see a firework party or not. I don't really like fireworks, especially not rockets. I shall never, ever play with fireworks again."

Angry Fairies

One morning Mrs Burrows the farmer's wife, took all the kitchen rugs into the garden and hung them, side by side, over the fence.

Whack! Whack! Whack! she went with the carpet beater.

Whack! Whack! Whack!

She sang merrily as she worked midst clouds of dust. She was very happy and as soon as one rug was clean she took it indoors, then came back and started on the next one.

Poor Mrs Burrows. How was she to know that the fairies had chosen that morning to sit among the flowers and chat about this and that!

The first whack she gave, made a sudden wind which straightaway blew off all the fairies' hats. They didn't like that very much. The second whack blew their hair into a tangle. They liked that even less.

The dust thrown out of the rug surrounded them in a cloud which made them all sneeze.

Atishoo! Atishoo! Atishoo! They sneezed in a chorus.

Atishoo! Atishoo! Atishoo!

"Stop! Stop!" they cried when they could speak, but Mrs Burrows who did not, indeed could not, hear the fairy voices, carried on with her work merrily.

Whack! Whack! Whack!

The fairies ran from the garden covered in dust, their eyes streaming, their hair in a tangle, their noses red, and their hats lost. Their tempers were very frayed and no wonder.

"Just you wait!" they shouted. "Just you wait! We'll be back and then you'll be sorry!"

Poor Mrs Burrows.

Back they came, that very night, bringing all their friends with them. Mrs Burrows and the farmer were asleep in bed, quite unaware that anything was wrong. Even if they had known what the fairies planned to do, they wouldn't have known how to prevent them. The fairies were going to lift the farmhouse up from its foundations and carry it to the bog where they were going to set it down in the muddiest stickiest, place they could find. That would teach the farmer's wife a lesson she would never forget when she went out next morning to milk the cows. First, they had to make the house ready to move.

They had all brought picks and shovels and wasted no time in getting to work.

Tap . . . tap . . . tapping at the mortar. Pick . . . pick . . . picking at the bricks.

The moon crept lazily across the sky. Presently they began to sing. Quietly at first, but then louder like a hundred humming bees. They worked their way all round the bottom of the house, loosening every brick and removing every nail.

Hum . . . hum . . . humming . . .

Tap . . . tap . . . tapping . . .

Pick . . . pick . . . picking . . .

121

The fairies were almost ready to lift the house and fly with it to the bog. Their humming grew more excited. The tap, tap, tapping grew quicker. The pick, pick, picking grew more insistent. Inside the house the farmer awoke. He listened.

"What's that I can hear?" he said, waking Mrs Burrows.

"You can't hear anything," she said sleepily. "Go back to sleep".

"I can hear something humming," he replied.

"It must be your ears," mumbled Mrs Burrows.

"I can hear something tapping . . ."

"It must be . . . SO CAN I!" said she, sitting up so suddenly her nightcap fell over her eyes.

Tap . . . tap . . . tap . . .

Pick . . . pick . . . pick . . .

"Probably a mouse scrambling under the roof," said the farmer drowsily.

"EEEK!" squealed his wife, who would face almost any danger, but who was terrified of mice and spiders. She dived under the blankets and hid her head.

At that moment the fairies loosened the last brick and the house was ready to lift. They threw down their picks and shovels with a mighty cheer. They unfolded their wings and prepared to hover. A hundred fairy hands slipped into the space between the house and its foundations.

They began to lift . . . upwards . . .

Inside the house everything began to shake and rock and slide.

"Whatever is happening?" cried the farmer's wife coming out from under the blankets.

"Ohhh . . ." she cried in dismay, as everything slid with a crash to the floor.

"Help!" she cried as the bed tipped over sideways. She flung her arms around the bed post and hung on to it tightly.

"What's happening? Is the world coming to an end? Is it an earthquake?" she wailed in terror.

"Of course not", said the farmer. "There must be a good reason for what is happening." Although at the time he couldn't think what it could be, when he looked towards the window and saw the stars falling to the ground.

He threw himself out of bed and crawled up the sloping floor towards the window. He caught hold of the windowsill, pulled himself up and looked outside. The ground was a lot further away than it should have been. He had never seen the top of the cow-shed from the bedroom window before and suddenly Mr Burrows was very frightened. Something very strange was happening . . . of that, he was sure.

"Heavens above" he cried. "Where are we going?"

The house was suddenly dropped to the ground with a thud! The fairies had been commanded to return to their kingdom by day-break. As the sun's rays peeped over the horizon, the fairies fled.

All the pots and pans in the kitchen jumped on their shelves and made a terrific clatter. All the plates and dishes fell off the dresser with an almighty crash.

Mrs Burrows slid UP the bed post and hit her head on the ceiling. The farmer shot upwards and then fell downwards bumping his chin on the windowsill.

Apart from one or two bruises and some broken plates there was no real damage done. The farmer and his wife never did find out what had really happened that night, or why it had happened and perhaps it was just as well.

The Three Billy-Goats Gruff

Once upon a time and far, far away in a land of beautiful mountains, fine green fields and sparkling streams, there lived three billy-goats. They were all named Gruff. The eldest and largest was called Big Billy-Goat Gruff; the next was called Middle Billy-Goat Gruff; and the youngest and smallest was called Tiny Billy-Goat Gruff. They had eaten all the grass in their field; they were hungry and getting thinner every day. So, they set off to find a better place, where they could eat and grow fat.

In the distance, on the other side of a wide stream, they saw a fine green field. The grass was thick and long; it was just what they wanted.

"We would get fat on that," said Tiny Billy-Goat Gruff in his little voice.

"Oh yes, we would," added Middle Billy-Goat Gruff in his soft voice.

"Then we must go at once," said Big Billy-Goat Gruff in his loud voice.

Over the stream was a wooden bridge to be crossed and under the bridge lived a troll. Now, a troll is a bad-tempered, ugly dwarf, who has big eyes and a long nose. He likes nothing better than eating goats for his supper. The children who lived in a village nearby stayed well away from the wooden bridge. Everyone was afraid of the ugly troll.

The three billy-goats looked at the bridge.

"What about the troll?" asked Tiny Billy-Goat Gruff in his little voice.

"Yes, what about the troll?" added Middle Billy-Goat Gruff in his soft voice.

"I have a plan," declared Big Billy-Goat Gruff in his loud voice. "Listen carefully." The three goats put their heads close together and they whispered to one another.

Tiny Billy-Goat Gruff was the first to reach the bridge. Trip, trip, trip . . . went his tiny hooves on the wooden boards.

Out came the ugly troll.

"Who is that tripping over my bridge?"

"Oh!" cried Tiny Billy-Goat Gruff in his little voice. "I am Tiny, the smallest Billy-Goat Gruff. I am going to that field over there to eat and grow fat."

"Ha!" roared the troll again. "No, you are not! I am going to eat YOU!"

Poor Tiny Billy-Goat began to shake. He trembled all over. "Oh, no! Do not bother with me . . . I am very small and I am so thin. Why not wait for the next Billy-Goat Gruff, he is much bigger and fatter."

The ugly troll stopped to think. "Very well!" he shouted. "Be off with you!"

So Tiny Billy-Goat Gruff quickly tripped over the bridge and into the fine green field.

Before long, up came Middle Billy-Goat Gruff. Trip, trot, trip, trot . . . went his hooves on the wooden boards.

Out came the ugly troll.

"Who is that?" he roared. "Who is that trotting over my bridge?"

"Oh!" cried Middle Billy-Goat Gruff in his soft voice. "I am Middle, the second Billy-Goat Gruff. I am on my way to the field over there to eat and grow fat."

"Ha!" roared the troll again. "No, you are not! I am going to eat YOU!"

Poor Middle Billy-Goat began to shake. He trembled all over.

"Oh, no! Do not bother with me . . . I am middle sized and really quite thin. Why not wait for Big Billy-Goat Gruff; he is really big and very much fatter."

The ugly troll stopped to think.

"Very well!" he shouted. "Be off with you!"

So Middle Billy-Goat Gruff quickly trotted over the bridge and into the fine green field.

Then came Big Billy-Goat Gruff. Trip, trot, tramp! Trip, trot, tramp . . . went his big hooves on the wooden boards.

Out came the ugly troll.

"Who is that?" he roared louder than ever. "Who is that tramping over my bridge?"

"Ah!" replied Big Billy-Goat Gruff in his loudest voice. "I am Big, the biggest Billy-Goat Gruff . . . and I am tramping over this bridge!"

The ugly troll roared with anger. "I am coming to get you!" he shouted. He moved a few steps towards the goat.

"Oh, no, you are not!" bellowed Big Billy-Goat Gruff. "I am coming to get YOU!"

He lowered his head and stamped his hooves. Tramp, tramp, TRAMP! Tramp, tramp, TRAMP!

They met in the middle of the bridge and a battle began. Big Billy-Goat Gruff prodded the ugly troll with his sharp horns. He picked him up and tossed him into the air. The ugly troll turned three somersaults before he fell with a splash into the deep water of the stream. He was never seen again.

So Big Billy-Goat Gruff tramped happily across the bridge and into the fine green field. All three billy-goats ate the sweet grass and grew fatter and fatter. The children in the village were happy. They could use the bridge and play in the fields, for the ugly old troll was gone forever.

A Pot of Gold

Patrick lived with his mother, and a cow and some hens, in a tiny cottage in the middle of Ireland. They were poor, but they were happy.

Every morning, as she blew on the peat fire to make it hot enough to cook their breakfast porridge, Patrick's mother would call, "Wake up, and get up, you lazy boy! You will never catch a leprechaun with your eyes closed."

Leprechauns are fairy shoemakers. They live in holes in the ground and between the roots of trees. They are said to be very rich, and wherever there is a leprechaun there is sure to be a pot of gold hidden somewhere close by.

There were leprechauns living near the cottage where Patrick lived with his mother. The wind had only to stop blowing for an instant and Patrick's keen ears could hear the sound of their tiny hammers hammering against leather.

131

It was Patrick's dearest wish to find a pot of gold. But first he had to find a leprechaun to show him where there was one hidden.

"If you happen to see a leprechaun," said Patrick's mother, at least once every day, "Do not take your eyes off him for a moment. If you do he will disappear and then you will never find a pot of gold."

One day, when Patrick was returning home after another fruitless search, he heard the sound of tapping. He looked down, and there, in the long grass at his feet, was a leprechaun. He was so busy, hammering away at a pair of hob-nailed boots, he hadn't noticed Patrick.

Patrick moved very quickly.

"Got you!" he cried as he caught the leprechaun in his hand.

"Let me go! Let me go!" shouted the leprechaun, struggling to get free.

"Tell me where your gold is hidden first!"

"G.g.gold . . . " The leprechaun turned very pale.

"Yes . . . tell me . . . or I will not let you go . . . not EVER!"

"Quick! Look behind you! There's a cow in the corn!" cried the leprechaun.

Just in time, Patrick remembered NOT to look.

"Ha . . . ha . . . you don't catch me that way. I won't take my eyes off you. Now where is your pot of gold?"

"I haven't got a pot of gold . . . " cried the leprechaun. "Quick! Look behind you! Your house is burning!"

Patrick almost did look THAT time.

"You're holding me too tight," squealed the leprechaun. "You're squeezing the breath out of me!"

"It's no good trying to trick me," said Patrick. "I'm not letting you go until you tell me where your gold is hidden."

"I'll show you where it is," said the leprechaun.

Patrick took off his braces, tied them round the leprechaun's waist and put him on the ground.

"NOW you can show me," said Patrick, without letting go of the braces. The leprechaun led him to a field of thistles.

"It's under THAT thistle," said the leprechaun, pointing to an extra prickly one "You'll need a spade to dig it up. You had better go home and get one."

Patrick thought quickly. How could he mark the thistle so that when he returned he would know which one it was.

"I'll put my garter round it," he said, and taking off one of the garters that held up his woollen socks, he placed it over the prickly thistle.

"NOW I'll go home and get the spade," he said, "and to make sure you don't play any tricks on me I'll put you in my pocket."

134

Patrick ran home, got a spade and ran all the way back. But when he reached the field, instead of digging, he sat down and howled. He cried and he sobbed. He held his head in his hands. Tears as big as raindrops rolled down his cheeks. Someone – I wonder who – had put a scarlet garter round every thistle in that field. There wasn't ONE thistle that did not have a scarlet garter for a belt. The leprechaun had tricked him after all. His mother had told him not to take his eyes off the leprechaun, hadn't she, and when Patrick put the leprechaun in his pocket that is exactly what he had done. He never saw another leprechaun and so he never found a pot of gold. His mother said, it was entirely his own fault.

The Enormous Turnip

Old Mr Poppascoff walked round his garden looking at his flowers and vegetables growing there. Then he saw the turnip!

"Come here, quickly," he called to his wife. "I only planted this yesterday. You can almost see it growing as you watch it."

"I don't like it," whispered his wife. "It's not right . . . it seems very strange to me."

Mr Poppascoff patted the turnip. "Now don't grow any more today . . . I'll come and see you in the morning."

Early the next morning, they woke to find the sun streaming in through the bedroom window. It was a lovely pale green. Mr Poppascoff padded over to the window in his bare feet.

"Oh dear!" he muttered. "Oh, my goodness me!"

His wife came to see what he was looking at. She had to stand on tiptoe, as the floor was very cold.

"That wretched turnip!" she cried. "I knew there was something wrong as soon as I saw it."

They went down into the garden to have a look at it. The turnip was enormous. They fell over backwards, just trying to see the top and there they sat, staring up at it.

"Whatever shall we do?" wailed Mrs Poppascoff.

"Eat it, I hope," said her husband. He went to fetch a ladder and a saw to cut it down. Up and up he climbed, while his wife held the ladder. Then, standing on the turnip top, he worked around, sawing the stalks off. Mrs Poppascoff sank beneath the falling leaves and was quite buried. She was not at all pleased.

After Mr Poppascoff had rescued her, they dragged all the leaves away. Then he tied one end of a rope round the stumps that were left and one end round his waist.

"Now, my dear," he said, "you push the turnip from that side. I will pull from this . . . we'll soon have it over."

But the turnip just wouldn't move.

"We'll both pull," said his wife.

So they pulled. Still the turnip wouldn't move.

Children coming home from school stopped to watch.

"Hi! . . . Johnny!" called Mr Poppascoff. "Come and help us pull up this turnip."

"Right," cried Johnny and he grabbed the old woman round her waist.

They all pulled. But still the turnip wouldn't move.

Johnny called to Sally, his sister, so she came to help.

"Pull!" cried Mr Poppascoff. " . . . and again!"

They dug in their heels, they got red in the face, but try as hard as they could, nothing would move the turnip.

"Call the dog," Johnny said.

So Mr Poppascoff whistled for Bess, the dog. She too helped to pull. Still the turnip would not move.

Then Tabitha the cat came and held on to the dog's tail.

"This time we'll do it," cried the old man. "Ready, steady, pull! Pull as hard as you can!"

But still the turnip would not move.

Suddenly, a little mouse raced across the garden. Down went Tabitha's paw, right across the mouse's tail.

"You live here doing nothing for your keep," said the cat. "Now get under that turnip and nibble through it, before I nibble you! . . . Then come and help to pull."

So the little mouse did just as he was told. Then he twisted his tail round the cat's tail and he started to pull.

Once! Twice! They pulled and pulled. Dirt and grit fell down on them like a shower of hailstones. Then all at once, the turnip shot out from the ground.

Everyone fell over in a heap. The little mouse pulled his tail away from the cat and ran. He didn't want to be squashed or nibbled.

Mr Poppascoff invited them all to supper.

"Bring your friends," he cried. "Bring everyone . . . You'll love my wife's turnip soup."

What a party! Everyone came and all the visitors had plenty to eat.

When they had gone, Bess and Tabitha lay snoozing on the mat, the little mouse was curled up in his hole and Mr Poppascoff and his wife sat watching the fire.

"It was a good party," said the old man.

"Very good," his wife agreed.

"No one could do better than that," he said. "Or grow such a turnip," he added. "I've never seen one like it before and there's plenty left."

"I don't want to see another turnip as long as I live!" cried the old woman. "I'm sick of turnips."

Silence . . . even the clock had stopped ticking. Slowly the old man turned and looked at her.

"My dear, you can't mean that . . . whatever is wrong with seeing turnips? They are quite beautiful . . . but as long as I live I'll never EAT ANOTHER."

Mr Poppascoff and his wife fell back in their chairs. They laughed till the tears ran down their cheeks. The animals grinned, the clock ticked again and the fire sparkled once more in the grate.

The Water Nixie

Sometimes deep in the forest, there are hidden streams where the Water Nixie lives. The Water Nixie is a sprite who likes to play tricks on children walking in the woods.

One day, a little boy and his sister, while out picking flowers, fell into just such a stream.

The Water Nixie was so pleased to have them in her power and set them both to work, cutting trees into logs and carrying heavy buckets of water. She gave them very little to eat and only cold water to drink. They were very unhappy and decided that somehow they must make their escape. They wondered how long it would be before their chance finally came.

At last, the Water Nixie decided to go out for a whole day.

"We must be quick," said the boy, but they were not quite quick enough for she came back sooner than they had expected. She was just in time to see the two children disappearing into the distance.

"Ha, ha," she laughed, not in the least bit troubled. "You think you will escape from me, do you? I'll soon have you back here where you belong. You don't really think I'm going to do the chores myself, do you?" She began to run towards the children with long, loping strides.

The children saw her coming and were very frightened. The only thing the little girl had in her pocket was a hairbrush which she threw on to the ground behind them. It turned into a hill of bristles so scratchy and so menacing it would have stopped the bravest knight.

"A hill of bristles will not stop ME!" laughed the Water Nixie, and she wriggled her way through without getting the slightest scratch.

"She's getting closer!" cried the girl. The boy took a comb from his pocket and threw that to the ground behind them. It turned into an enormous ridge of closely packed spikes, pointed and sharp as darning needles. Nothing but the wind could get between them.

"A ridge of spikes will not stop ME!" laughed the Water Nixie. To the children's dismay she jumped on top of the ridge. Holding out her arms to balance herself, she hopped from spike to spike with hardly a wobble.

"What did I tell you?" she shouted as she jumped down on the other side. "I'll soon have you back where you belong!"

All the children had left to defend themselves was a small mirror. They threw it to the ground behind them. It turned into a hill that was as slippery and sheer as the largest iceberg.

"A hill of mirrors will never stop ME!" laughed the Water Nixie.

This time she was wrong. She slithered and she slipped and slid. She couldn't find a foothold anywhere, and everywhere she looked she saw her own reflection mocking and taunting her.

"You haven't escaped from me yet!" she cried. The Water Nixie ran home for an axe, but by the time she had returned and chopped a way through the middle of the hill the children were far ahead. It was impossible for her to catch up with them, even by the use of magic. She had to go back to doing the hard work herself and wait until another child fell into her stream.

Long Nose

Once there was a miller who had three sons, and a farmer who had a pretty daughter. One day, Roland, the eldest of the miller's three sons, said, "I am going to ask Margaret to marry me today."

In the lane leading to the farmhouse he met Old Molly. She was wrinkled and bent, and very ugly. Unkind people called her Mad Molly, and said she was a witch.

"Good day!" said Old Molly. "And where might you be going?"

Roland stuck his nose in the air and walked past her as though she wasn't there. It was a wonder he didn't fall over his own feet.

"No!" said Margaret, when Roland proposed. "I will NOT marry you."

A few days later, Robert, the second of the miller's sons said, "I am going to ask Margaret to marry ME today." He was quite sure he would succeed where his brother had failed.

Old Molly was gathering primroses in the lane leading to the farmhouse.

"Good day!" she said politely. "And where might you be going?"

Robert stuck HIS nose into the air and pretended to look at a bird which wasn't there.

"No! I will not marry YOU!" said Margaret when Robert asked her to marry him.

Robin was the third, and youngest, of the miller's three sons. He was kind and strong, but he had one fault. At least HE thought it was a fault. He had a very, long nose. A very, VERY long nose – the kind of nose that people laugh at. He wanted Margaret to marry HIM.

He met Old Molly by the farmhouse gate.

"Good day!" said Old Molly. "And where are you going?"

"On a hopeless errand," sighed Robin. "How can I expect Margaret to marry me when I have such a ridiculous nose. She has refused my two brothers, she is sure to refuse me."

"That's where you're wrong!" said Old Molly. "She shall marry you." She took a ring from one of her bony fingers and gave it to him. "Put that on and say 'Bless it'," she said.

Robin put the ring on his own finger.

"Go on, say what I told you to say," said Old Molly.

"Bless it," said Robin, and straight away his nose shrank half an inch. It really was quite surprising the way it happened, and how handsome it made him look.

"If Margaret refuses to marry you," said Old Molly, "Say 'Drat it' and then HER nose will grow half an inch. It will make her so ugly she will be glad to marry you."

"Thank you," said Robin. "I'll ask her straight away."

When he got to the farmhouse Margaret was out.

"I'll wait," he said, and sat down. He began to day-dream and presently he closed his eyes.

Now, it so happened that there was another visitor at the farmhouse that day. He was an old miser who never spent a penny unless he had to. He was very rich, and Margaret's father, who thought being rich was important, wanted Margaret to marry him. The miser saw Robin sitting with his eyes closed and he saw the ring on Robin's finger.

'I'll take that, and give it to Margaret, then I will not have to spend money buying her a ring,' he thought. And very slyly, and very carefully, he took the ring from Robin's finger and slipped it onto his own for safe keeping.

Robin might have had his
eyes closed, but he wasn't asleep.
He knew exactly what the miser
was doing. As soon as the ring
was on the miser's finger he
whispered, "Drat it."

"OOOH," said the miser.
"Something has stung me!" He put
his hand up to feel his nose,
which was – you must have guessed –
half an inch longer than it had
been a moment before. "OOOOOH!
Something is making my nose swell!"

"Drat it!" whispered Robin
again. The miser's nose grew
another half inch. "Drat it!"
whispered Robin.

"What's happening?" shouted
the miser as his nose grew even
longer. "I must find a doctor at
once." So away he rushed, trying
to cover his nose with his hands.
It wasn't easy because the end kept
poking through his fingers.

147

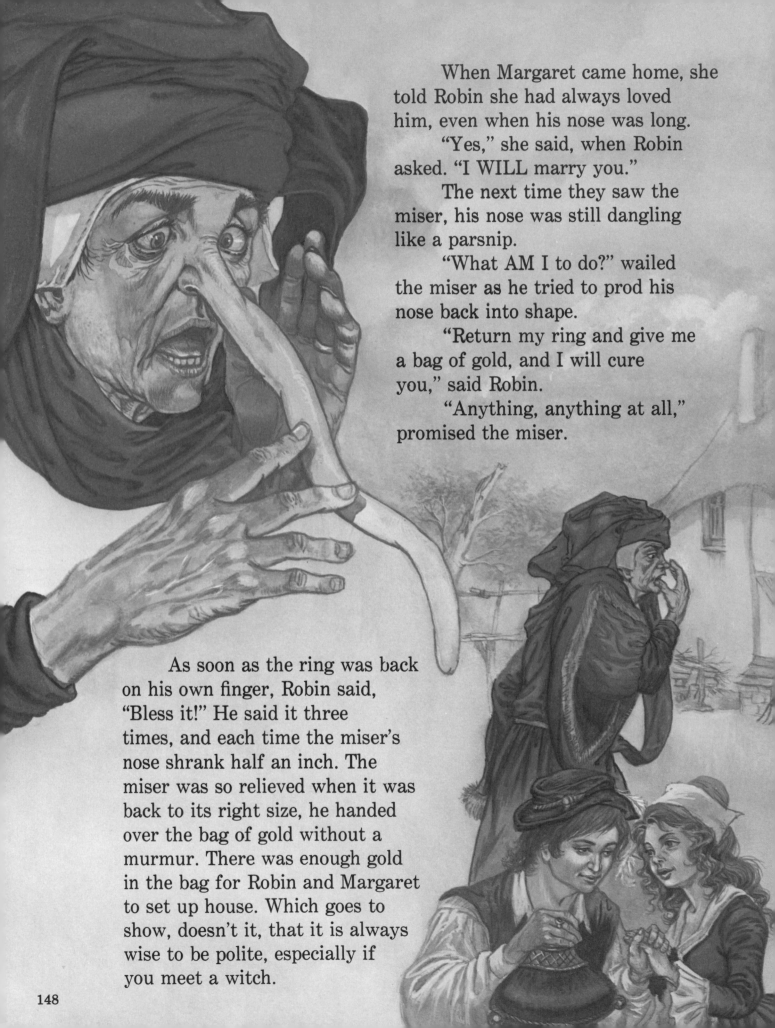

When Margaret came home, she told Robin she had always loved him, even when his nose was long.

"Yes," she said, when Robin asked. "I WILL marry you."

The next time they saw the miser, his nose was still dangling like a parsnip.

"What AM I to do?" wailed the miser as he tried to prod his nose back into shape.

"Return my ring and give me a bag of gold, and I will cure you," said Robin.

"Anything, anything at all," promised the miser.

As soon as the ring was back on his own finger, Robin said, "Bless it!" He said it three times, and each time the miser's nose shrank half an inch. The miser was so relieved when it was back to its right size, he handed over the bag of gold without a murmur. There was enough gold in the bag for Robin and Margaret to set up house. Which goes to show, doesn't it, that it is always wise to be polite, especially if you meet a witch.

148

Pancake Tommy

If you ever meet the Magic Clucker Bird, strange things may happen, as they did to Pancake Tommy on his way to the farm. Pancake Tommy wasn't his real name, but everybody called him that because he was always eating pancakes. He ate pancakes for breakfast, pancakes for lunch and pancakes for supper. However hard he tried, he couldn't stop eating pancakes. He was never asked to parties because he didn't like ice cream and he didn't like sandwiches or even birthday cake.

"Try some of my custard pie," his mother would say. "It's made with eggs, just like the pancakes."

"No thank you – just pancakes," Pancake Tommy would reply.

"Try some of my chocolate sponge cake," his Granny would say. "It's made with eggs, like the pancakes."

"No thank you – just pancakes," Pancake Tommy would reply.

"Well," said his mother, "if that's all you're going to eat every day of your school holidays, we'll need plenty of eggs from Mrs Bond's farm."

The next morning, carrying a basket for the eggs, Pancake Tommy went down the lane to the farm. He had nearly reached the end of it when he heard a strange sound coming from behind the hedge.

Cluck–cluck–cluck–Ker! Cluck–cluck–cluck–Ker!

It sounded just like one of Mrs Bond's hens laying an egg, and Tommy thought he would pick it up on the way back.

So, after he had been to the farm, he went to look for it. There in the ditch was a big brown egg. Beside it, stood the funniest bird he'd ever seen. Its purple body had yellow stripes and its wings were green. It had a very long neck and three legs instead of two.

It was the Magic Clucker Bird and it spoke: "Why do you want to take my egg?"

"To make more pancakes for me to eat," said Pancake Tommy. "But I wish I could stop eating them, so that I could go to birthday parties."

"Then I will help you," said the Magic Clucker Bird. "Take my egg home, it will make a flying pancake . . . just follow that, wherever it goes."

Then the Magic Clucker Bird flew away and Pancake Tommy picked up his basket and carried the big brown egg in his hand all the way home.

"Will you please make a pancake with this big egg, mother?" asked Pancake Tommy, and she did. As soon as she put the pancake on the plate, the Clucker Bird's magic began to work. The pancake rose up from the plate, flew round the kitchen and out of the door. Pancake Tommy followed.

"Where are you going?" called his mother, but he did not answer. He just followed the flying pancake as the Magic Clucker Bird had told him.

On and on flew the pancake. Then it came to rest in the lane near Mrs Bond's farm. It began to grow bigger and bigger as Pancake Tommy watched. The Magic Clucker Bird came from behind the hedge and said: "Sit on top of it, you'll be quite safe."

Pancake Tommy climbed up and soon he was being carried away on top of the pancake. It flew over Mrs Bond's farm, over mountains and over seas, until it came down to rest in a very strange land.

Pancake Tommy looked at the people standing all round him, their faces as flat as pancakes. The ladies wore flat pancake hats and they all wore flat pancake shoes.

Down the steps of the Town Hall came a very important-looking person – it was the Mayor, and he walked over to the flying pancake.

"Where am I?" asked Pancake Tommy.

"Where you belong, of course," replied the Mayor. "You are in the land of the Pancake people – you must come and meet some of them. Follow me." And Pancake Tommy followed him.

"This is Pancake Polly – she makes our Pancake hats and this is Pancake Pete, he makes our Pancake shoes," said the Mayor. "We all have jobs to do here. You can make Pancake wheels for our buses or you can make pancakes for us all to eat."

"But I don't want to stay here," said Pancake Tommy in a frightened voice.

"Of course, you must stay – you eat pancakes all day, don't you? So do we," said the Mayor. "That's why all our faces look like them."

"But I don't want to stay here," said Pancake Tommy once again.

The Mayor took no notice and spoke this time in an angry voice: "Well, which job are you going to do then?"

"I'll help to make the pancakes for you all to eat," replied Pancake Tommy.

He was taken to help the cook, in the biggest kitchen he'd ever seen. There were baskets and baskets full of eggs, sacks and sacks full of flour and salt, and bottles and bottles of milk. Pancake Tommy mixed the pancakes, then the cook popped them in the pan. They worked very hard, until there was not one egg left, but lots and lots of pancakes standing in piles on the table.

"Where did the eggs come from to make so many pancakes?" asked Pancake Tommy.

"The Magic Clucker Bird lays them and it's time we collected some more," said the cook.

Pancake Tommy followed her out of the kitchen and over to a big shed.

From the shed came the noise he'd heard before in the lane.
Cluck–cluck–cluck–Ker.
Cluck–cluck–cluck–Ker.

The cook knocked on the door and out stepped the brightly-coloured Magic Clucker Bird. It walked across to the kitchen without speaking to either of them, so they followed.

The Magic Clucker Bird looked at the piles of pancakes on the table and asked: "How many pancakes did you make?"

"Three thousand and two," said Pancake Tommy, "but I don't want to make any more. I don't want to stay here. Please may I go home?"

"Come with me to the Town Hall and we'll see what the Mayor says about it," said the Magic Clucker Bird.

The Mayor and the Magic Clucker Bird whispered together. Then the Mayor looked at Pancake Tommy and said: "Three thousand and two pancakes. Three thousand for the Pancake people and two for you to eat, while you're waiting for the Magic Clucker Bird to lay another special egg."

At last, the Flying Pancake was ready. The Pancake people crowded round to watch it grow big enough for Pancake Tommy to climb up and sit on top of it.

The Mayor said: "You'll soon be home, but unless you stop eating pancakes all day long, we shall bring you back to the land of the Pancake people."

The Magic Clucker Bird called out again, "Cluck–cluck–cluck–Ker. Cluck–cluck–cluck–Ker."

The Pancake people waved as the pancake rose up in the air. It flew over the sea, over the mountains and came down to rest again in the lane near Mrs Bond's farm. Pancake Tommy stepped down and watched it fly away.

Mrs Bond called out to him: "Wherever have you been? Your mother has been looking for you."

Pancake Tommy never answered her. He just walked slowly home, thinking he'd never eat pancakes again.

"Glad you're back," said his mother. "Your pancakes are ready for you to eat."

"No, thank you," replied Pancake Tommy. "I think I'll have some of your custard pie and Granny's chocolate sponge cake."

The next day, he had some ice cream and the day after that, he had sandwiches and cream cakes. Now he goes to lots of birthday parties where he eats sausage rolls, and fruit pies, but no pancakes at all. No one calls him Pancake Tommy anymore, just Tommy Brown.

Gold

There's gold in the meadows
And gold in the trees;
It shines on the buttercups,
It shimmers on leaves.
There are golden-eyed daisies
And marigolds to pluck;
Bright gold of the daffodils
Pale gold of the duck.

There's gold on the eagle
And small crested bird;
There are fine golden fishes
In thousands, I've heard.
There's gold that men dig for
Down in the earth;
Then bury in Banks
And count up its worth.

But listen, Great Sun,
As you sink in the west:
Your gold so warm
Is the loveliest.